Self-Published:

12~12~2012

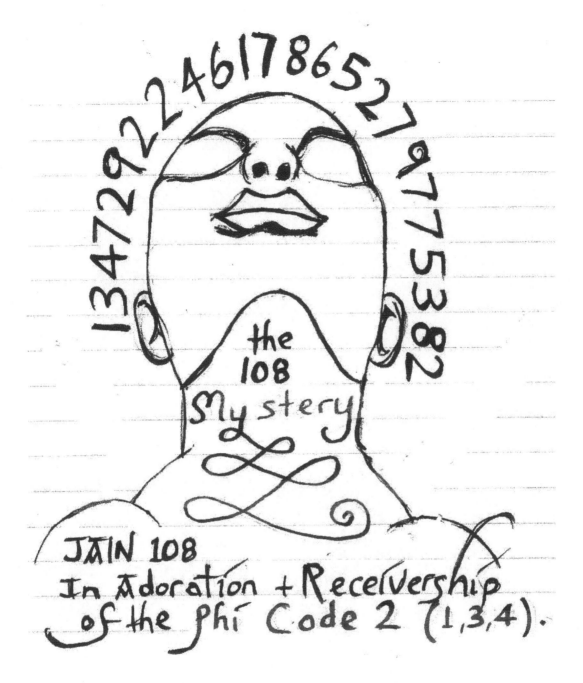

the
108
Mystery

JAIN 108
In Adoration + Receivership
of the Phi Code 2 (1,3,4).

in adoration of the paraphysical phi code 2

ISBN: 978-0-9757484-4-2

DEDICATION

To all my Phirends & PhiloMorphs
(Lovers Of Form or Shape)

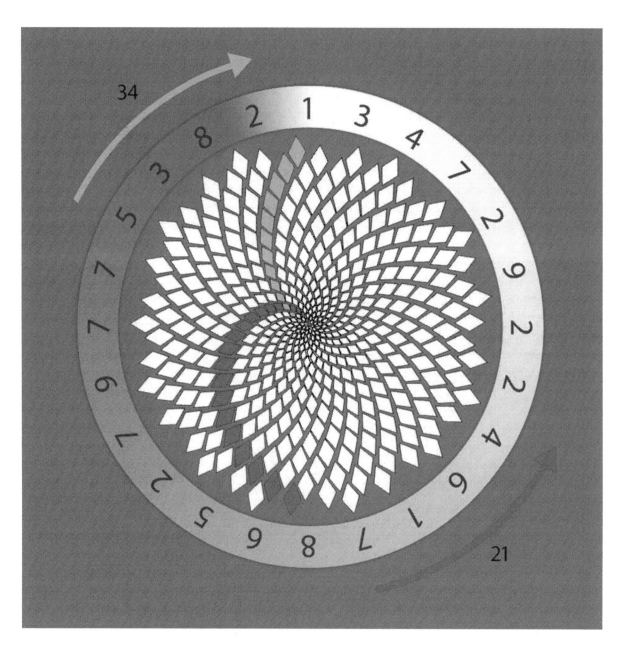

(Thanks to Aaron Lutze who created this composition in PhotoShop
and for all his generous support over the Years).

In UNICITY, we do not Love Others, rather, We Are Them.

CONTENTS IN BRIEF

Legend:
CH = Chapter

The real question is not whether life exists after death.
The real question is whether you are alive before death.
Osho

CONTENTS IN FULL

Legend:
CH = Chapter

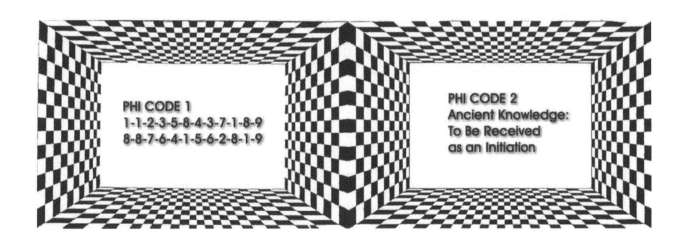

PHI CODE 1
1-1-2-3-5-8-4-3-7-1-8-9
8-8-7-6-4-1-5-6-2-8-1-9

PHI CODE 2
Ancient Knowledge:
To Be Received
as an Initiation

~INTRODUCTION~
TO THE 108 PHI CODE TRANSMISSIONS

PHIomETRY:

It so happened that I drew the short straw
for the release of the Phi 108 Codes.
It comes at a time when humanity needs
to be introduced to this lost topic that I call Phi-Ometry.
JAIN

Jain's insights into Sri 108 will become the cynosure of every mathematician's eye. How remarkable, though simple, that the compression or digital reduction of the Fibonacci Sequence reveals 3 distinct 24 Repeating Patterns aka The 3 Phi Dials.

This Phi Code 2, (or really Pine Code 2) the Powers of Phi, is the Hope Diamond in my library of 1,000 lives. It's about learning to live in the Phi Code 108 Architecture, to be Self-Organized which is really about 2 Pine Cones learning how to kiss noses, it's about a stream of water becoming so Self-Aware it forms the classic PonyTail.

"GOLDEN RATIO"
has it's letters rearranged (anagram) to form:
"GOD RELATION"

"GOLDEN SECTION"
has it's letters rearranged (anagram) to form:
"IS TO ENCODE LENGTH"

"GOLDEN MEAN"
has it's letters rearranged (anagram) to form:
"DEMON ANGEL"

(these 3 quotes are taken from: www.goldennumber.net)

Jain's numerous books on Sri 108 questions, exposes and reveals all the true hidden mathematics that is not being taught in schools; it is a dart thrown in the face of traditional and national maths-curriculum maker's skullduggery, to keep our innocent children uneducated and mis-informed. The sequel to this book, will be The Book Of Phi, Volume 7: "IS PI A LIE" clearly showing that the traditional value of Pi 3.141592 is only the limit of the circle formed from billions of triangular wedges, but it does not account for the area under the curve, which means that Pi must be a fraction more than what is stated, and it's true value 3.144... is based on the square root of the Phi (1.272... equates to the height of Cheops Pyramid, when the base apothem equals 1 unit).

In the same manner and meaning regarding Napoleon's words when he first entered the extraordinary Chartres Cathedral:
"CHARTRES IN NO PLACE FOR AN ATHEIST"
as it instills a most holy atmosphere to all who behold it's majesty, similarly, these 3 Phi 108 Codes (as will be seen in the sequel The Book Of Phi, Volume 6) and all their super symmetry allures us back to Nature's wit. This is no place for someone ignorant of mathematics. The monuments dedicated to Mary Magdalene, the true wife of Jesus and the children they bore, is as heretical and fantastic as are these forbidden Phi Codes. It's time that the Light shone thru these glorious leadlights and canonize the cobwebbed facts.
Jain

ODE TO PHI CODE 2 (PC134)

Phi Code (PC112) has been revealed and released but Phi Code 2 needed super technology to prove it's recursiveness of 108ness. It's memory has been stored in ancient pre-Lemurian crystal books (best described as memory storage devices that were in the shape of spheres whose pages turned!). Thus Phi Code 2 has permission now to be published or reborn after a dormant phase of 108 Earthly cycles, waiting for the consciousness of the planet to wake up and for humanities technology to reach a critical height (where the Square Root of 5 could be known beyond 77 decimal places!). Thanks to CCalc (my Console Calculator) a free downloadable internet calculator with over 77 dp precision, was found and proven by Jain 108, he cracked the 2nd Phi Code, based on the Powers of Phi (meaning we take the Golden Mean of 1.618033... and keeping multiplying by this number by squaring, cubing, fourth powers, fifth powers etc). Such forbidden God Knowledge (really it is akin to the Harmonic Stairway to Heaven) is now available. "Be careful how you use this" warns Jain. "If you translate this Repeating 24 Pattern say into Sound, let your Song be Love".

This 5th Book of Phi is indeed a documentary Treasure, the culmination of many a years of pattern-hunting, emerging out of the dust and mould of damp vaults in a locked and secret library... now in Jain's evolutionary trusteeship.

Jain (the antiquarian futuristic mathematician and artist).

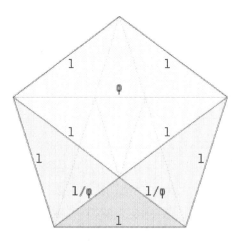

The Phi Rhombus.
nb: within the pentagon is a perfect Rhombus
(like a diamond form) at the top part of the image.
Its sides are all 1 unit but the main diagonal is Phi (1.618...)

~ CHAPTER 1 ~

108 PHI CODE 2
AS MYSTIC COGGED WHEELS
AND OTHER CIRCULAR
INTERPRETRATIONS

Chapter One Includes:

- How Is Phi Code 2 (PC:1,3,4) Derived?

- Plotting PC2 volumetrically onto a 24 toothed wheel

- Plotting the 12 Pairs of PC2 from the Centre and moving Outwards.

- Plotting the 12 Pairs of PC2 from Outer Rim and towards the Centre.

- Phi Code 2 Voltage Differences of the Pairs + the Phi-Prime Connection

- Plotting the 12 Pairs of PC2 into the Circle divided into 108 Segments.

- Comparison of the First 2 Phi Codes

- Plotting Phi Code 2 upon the 9 Point Circle

- Derivation of the Harmonic 216 + the Mystical Squaring of the Circle

- A New Model: How to Uni-Phi

HOW IS PHI CODE 2 (PC:1,3,4) DERIVED?

We start by selecting the two numbers 1 & 3 as the first two terms of an infinitely additive sequence, and add those two terms give 1+3=4. We now have the Sequence 1,3,4 and to get the 4th term we add the last two digits which is 3+4=7. We now have the Sequence 1,3,4,7 and so on... A "Fibonacci-Like Sequence" can be any infinitely additive sequence that starts with any 2 random numbers. It turns out that any such choice of numbers all produce Wheels of 24, that sum to 108, and can be found on only 3 distinct Wheels or Dials, thus the term "The 3 Phi Codes" (see next book: The Book Of Phi, vol 6).

1, 3, 4, 7, 11, 18, 29, 47, 76, 123, 199, 322, 521, 843, 1364, 2207, 3571, 5778, 9349, 15127, 24476, 39603, 64079, 103,682

Here are the first 24 Numbers of this Fibonacci-Like Sequence:

Fig 1a

The first 24 Fibonaccoid Numbers for Phi Code 2

By continual subtraction of 9 from all of these Fibonacci Numbers (which is the real definition of Digit Sums or Digital Compression, we convert large numbers to single digits. eg: Look at the 7th number in the sequence above, which is 29 and continue to add the sum of these two digits:

Ie: 29=2+9=11 and 11 further reduces to 1+1=2 thus the number 29 can be seen to be expressed below as the single digit 2. It's really the Remainder after dividing by 9. ie: 29 divided by 9 = 9+9+9+2.

The 24 Repeating Pattern, derived from the Digital Compression of the above into single digits from 1 to 9 is: Here are the first 24 Numbers of this PC2:

1	3	4	7	2	9	2	2	4	6	1	7	8	6	5	2	7	9	7	7	5	3	8	2

Fig 1b

Powers Of Phi Code 108: an Infinitely Repeating 24 Pattern
Based on the Compression of the Powers Of Phi into Single Digits. This one is termed Multi-Dimensional, aka PHI CODE 2.

Let us now explore what these same infinitely repeating 24 numbers of the Phi Code appear like when plugged into a wheel with 9 concentric rings to define the cogs of a wheel as the pattern unfolds.

Before starting this chapter, I am creating a new jargon here, coining the expressions, "PHI CODE 1" and "PHI CODE 2" and "PHI CODE 3"
to now represent the three long-winded titles:

"PHI CODE 1" = The Phi Code 108 based on the Compression of the Fibonacci Numbers, the Linear Sequence of 24 Repeating Numbers and whose Pair (9,9) is situated in the 12th column or at the end of the 12 Paired Sequence. The Sequence starts with 1,1,2 thus it is summarized to: PC1(1,1,2).

"PHI CODE 2" = The Phi Code 108 based on the Compression of the Powers Of Phi Numbers, the Multi-Dimensional Sequence of 24 Repeating Numbers and whose Pair (9,9) is in the 6th Column of the 12 Paired Sequence.
The Sequence starts with 1,3,4 thus it is summarized to: PC2(1,3,4).

"PHI CODE 3" = The Phi Code 108 based on the Compression of the Fibonacci-like Numbers starting with 1 and 4, the Linear Sequence of 24 Repeating Numbers and whose Pair (9,9) is in the 4th Column of the 12 Paired Sequence. The Sequence starts with 1,4,5 thus it is summarized to: PC3(1,4,5).

1	3	4	7	2	9	2	2	4	6	1	7
8	6	5	2	7	9	7	7	5	3	8	2

Fig 1c

The Powers Of Phi Infinitely repeating 24 Pattern

rearranged in it's 2x12 format.

shown as two rows of 12, with vertical Pairs Summing to 9.

Highlighting the intriguing central pair of double Nines.

What does it really mean?

The purpose of the exercise is to merely **"Translate Number Into Art"** and find practical applications of this data for our future technologies to remain in resonance with Nature's choice of numbers or natural frequencies.

Fig 1d

Space to write in the 24 Repeating Pattern for Phi Code 2,

to develop your memory power.

Write in the 24 Repeating Pattern for the Powers of Phi, above in the 24 squares. This is just to get you acquainted with numbers as you will be working with them a lot in this book. This is the linear format. On the next pages in Fig 1e and Fig 1f, you will write again, by memory, the same 24 numbers into 2 various wheel formats.

Fig 1e

Worksheet 1: MEMORIZING PHI CODE 2

To get a feel what it is like to simply write out these 24 repeating numbers of the Phi Code 1, "Off By Heart" write these numbers from the top petal, going clockwise, and do it in a manner where you have memorized these numbers. eg: by memorizing the first set of 12 numbers of Phi Code 1, you already know that the second set of 12 numbers are the complementary pairs of 9. I find it easier to remember the first set of 12 numbers in triplets, like this:

1 3 4 - 7 2 9 - 2 2 4 - 6 1 7

This page has the same worksheet (Fig 1f) as the previous one, but with a different image of this 24 Repeating Pattern, for you to write the Wheel of 24 Digits of PC2 again. (Image is a typical **Spirograph** pattern, having here 24 petals).

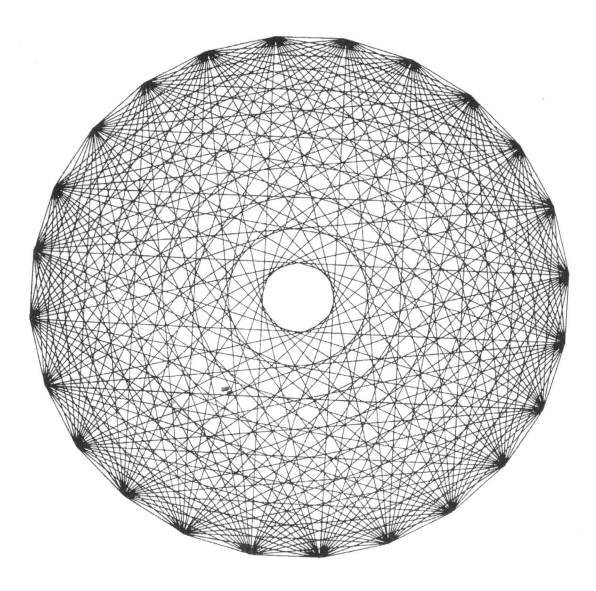

Fig 1f

Worksheet 2: MEMORIZING PHI CODE 2

(Image is a **Mystic Rose of 24 Points**: as all points are inter-connected)

PLOTTING PC2 VOLUMETRICALLY
ONTO A 24 TOOTHED WHEEL

To be able to understand Fig 2a, and for you to actually draw it for yourself, you are required to visualize the original wheel as a pure circle, as our starting point, with 9 concentric rings around it, and 24 radials, which will capture all the 24 numbers to be drawn as bar segments as in a bar graph or as pure arcs then shaded in as a circle segment of 1/24th. Each blackened-in arc length depends on the value given from 1 to 9.

Or, you can visualize the original wheel as a pure 24-sided polygon (a male shape, as in sacred geometry, any straight line is considered male, and any curved lines are considered female). Technically, the name of this shape is called a "IcosaTetraGon" (Icosa-tetra-gon, from the greek words: "Icosa" means "20", "tetra" means "4" and "gon" means "side". This would form a shape that overall appears like a spider's web.

To define the Original wheel, upon which you will draw in the cogs or wave-like undulations, whether as curved female arcs or straight male lines, I have decided, in the following worksheet, to draw in the 24 straight lines to form the Icosatetragon. As you translate the following 24 Repeating Pattern of the 108 Phi Code into this wheel, it is your choice whether you use arcs or straight lines to complete the pattern as shown in Fig 2b.

You may want to photocopy Fig 2a several times and work upon these copies, leaving Fig 2a untouched as your master copy.

To start plugging these 24 numbers into the wheel, you need to mark the top most or northern point of the wheel, in Fig 2a, call it 1; then going clockwise, the next number is 3, then 4 then 7 then 11 then 18 etc... It's like a clock of 24 divisions. For every phi code number from 1 to 24, it will be sketched as a length, eg: the number 3 would mean you are required to colour in or sketch 3 of the 9 rings. That is how the 24 teeth of the wheel are formed. It is like a horizontally flat bar graph that is joined end to end to make a circle.

Upon Fig 2a, your first worksheet, write in a clockwise, circular fashion the 24 numbers for Phi Code 2. I have shown the numbers in their triplet form:

1-3-4 – 7-2-9 – 2-2-4 – 6-1-7 – 8-6-5 – 2-7-9 – 7-7-5 - 3-8-2

and mark these numbers around the largest circle.

This way you lessen your chance of making a mistake. Then shade it and observe the cogged wheel or teething created. Does it give you another view or perspective of the Phi Codes. If we can see them here as surface areas, it means also that we can see them as volumes!

Upon Fig 2a, plot the Phi Code 2 being the 24 Repeating Pattern for the Powers Of Phi. This will be created on the next page Fig 2b, the solution.

(Indian Jain Hand:
notice it has a Wheel of 24 rays, similar to the national Indian Flag).

JAIN MATHEMAGICS WORKSHEET 2007
"PHI CODE AS A
MYSTIC COGGED WHEEL".

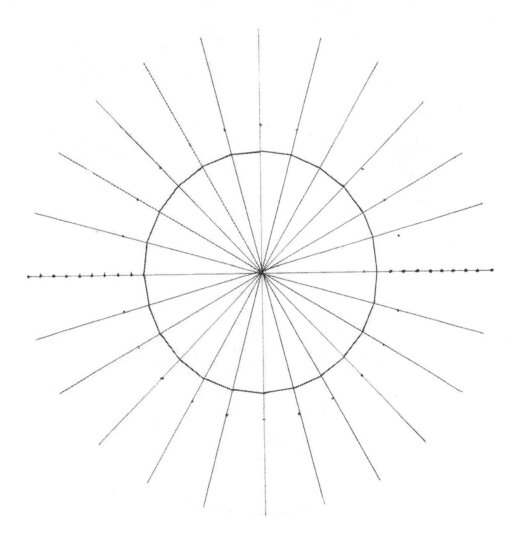

the infinitely repeating 24 Pattern. Jain 108

Fig 2a

Worksheet for Plotting the 24 Repeating Phi Code 2 onto a wheel or
24-sided IcosaTetraGon to show the Circular Cogged or Teethed Pattern.

The student is to draw their own 9 Concentric Circles.

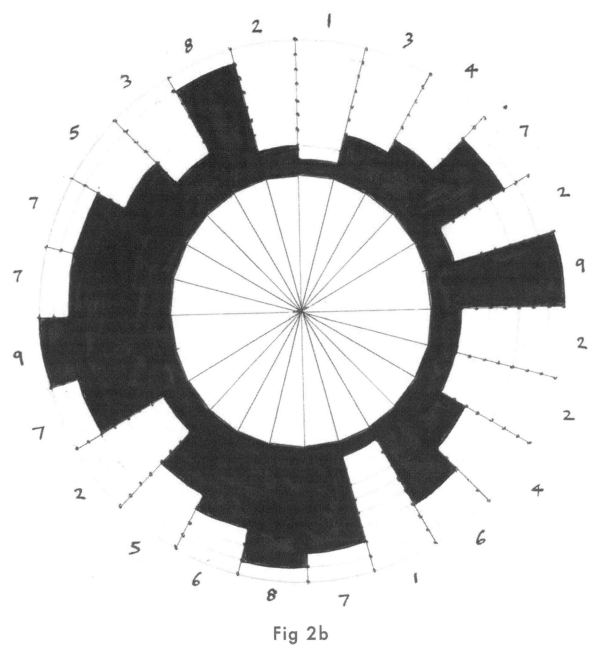

Fig 2b

Solution: The Mystic Cogged Wheel,

Based on Jain's Infinitely Repeating 24 Pattern of the Phi Code 2.

DID YOU KNOW that this second phi code sequence is identical to the stock marketeer's Lucas Numbers!

1	3	4	7	2	9	2	2	4	6	1	7	8	6	5	2	7	9	7	7	5	3	8	2

With our X-Ray eyes, we the Pattern Hunters, are ready to pierce through this data via the supreme art of translating numbers into art. The Left Brain of Numbers is thus tempted to conjoin or **Uni-Phi** with the Right Brain of Art to allow Revelation to make it's creative and intuitive presence. The fun now starts, as we have created a certain structure, like in Fig 2b, but we do not know the outcome of what designs that will emerge, this is the exciting part, the not knowing, but on a higher level, we already know intuitively that something pretty will be evoked, it's a certainty, we know that anything based on phi is the mathematics of beauty and can predict some strange yantra to be downloaded. ("**Yantra**" is a sanskrit word that literally means "instrument" or a form of "**Power Art**", the very penned stroke of the psycho-active lines conduct certain psychic electron flows in the quantum physics of consciousness; "Yantra" is plural for the single "Yantram").

"You never change things by fighting the existing reality.

To change something,

build a new model

that makes the existing model obsolete."

- Buckminster Fuller

PLOTTING THE 12 PAIRS OF PC2
FROM THE CENTRE AND MOVING OUTWARDS

JAIN · MATHEMAGICS WORKSHEET.
GRID / TEMPLATE for PLOTTING the
12 PAIRS of 9ness. (Using 10° radials)

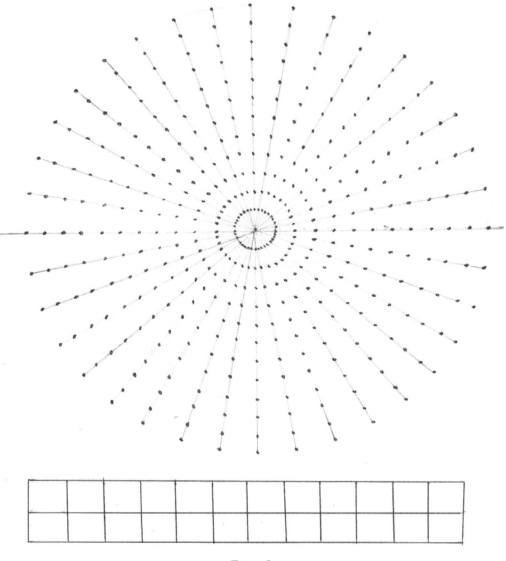

Fig 3a

Grid Template for Plotting the 12 Pairs of 9ness,
for the Phi Code 2.
The Order of Plotting the Pairs can be geared
from the Centre and Outwards or in reverse order:
from the Outer Rim and working towards the Centre.

In Fig 3a above, I have given you just the original grid work of dots, achieved by dividing the circle into 10 degree radials or increments. That means dividing the circle into 36 divisions. You can use 18 divisions of 20 degree, but to get the precise geometry that you will appreciate later when you actually draw the Pairs for yourself, you will realize that it is better to divide again and work with the 10 degree spokes.

In Fig 3a you will need to write down, in the space provided at the bottom of the worksheet, the 12 Pairs of 9 for Phi Code 2, actually you are able to remember this Pattern of numbers and not need to copy them from a written table. I do advise that the serious student commit this Phi Code 2 to memory, embed it in your Heart.

Visualize that the circle is really two joined hemispheres or semi-circles. The top or northern semi-circle of Fig 3b will carry the top half of the 12 Pairs of 9, that is, starting firstly from the centre and going outwards, you will be required to plot the numbers:

1 - 3 - 4 - 7 - 2 - 9 - 2 - 2 - 4 - 6 - 1 - 7

Conversely, you will be required to plot

8 - 6 - 5 - 2 - 7 - 9 - 7 - 7 - 5 - 3 - 8 - 2

into the bottom half or lower or southern semi-circle.

All plotting of numbers or pairs is achieved by shading in the segments that are defined.

To start drawing:

You need to have in front of you another photocopy of Fig 3a, or several copies, it being the basic template where I have divided the circle in 36 divisions at 10 degree radials. It really contains two hemi-spheres, aligned to north and south pole, indicated by the Zero written above and below the circle. The horizontal diameter of the circle is what divides the circle into half, each half will relate to parts or sets of 12 digits of the Powers of Phi Code.

In Fig 3a you will need to write down, in the space provided at the bottom of the worksheet, the Powers Of Phi's 12 Pairs of 9.

Notice also in the next diagram of Fig 3c, I have achieved half of the project at hand, by merely outlining the 12 Pairs of 9 that are boxed in at the bottom of the worksheet.

Notice also that there are 2 semi-circles of numbers ranging from zero to 9 on the outermost circle. It's like a compass, the "0" is the top of the diagram, and there are two number "1"s on the left and right of this zero northern or zenith point. Thus if you wanted to shade in a segment that was defined by "1" in the Phi Code, you can easily see the boundaries of this segment.

Notice also that the Central Double 9 Pair of the Powers Of Phi Code, is two semi-circular segments meeting which therefore creates a full ring in the middle of the whole mandala.

When fully sketched in, Fig 3b will look like this StarGate: Fig 3d.

Contemplating the **multi-dimensional**
POWERS Of PHI aka Phi Code 2 or PC2.

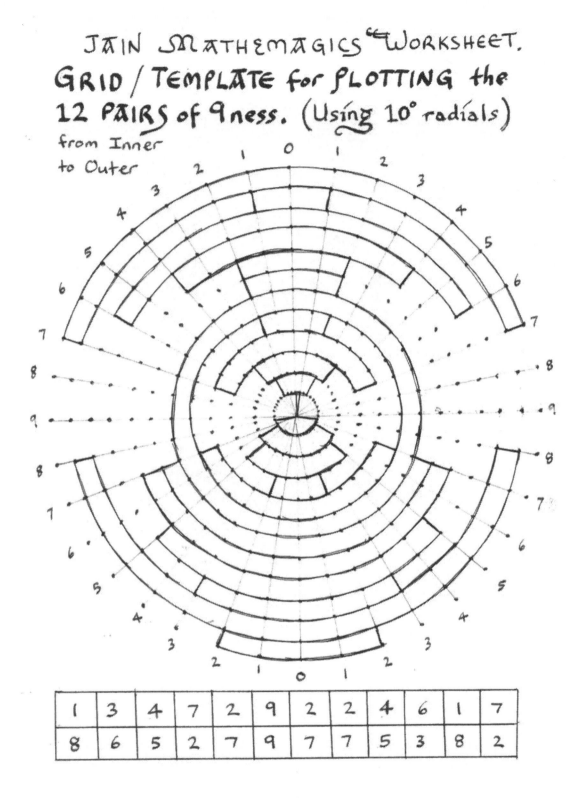

JAIN MATHEMAGICS "WORKSHEET.
GRID / TEMPLATE for PLOTTING the
12 PAIRS of 9ness. (Using 10° radials)
from Inner
to Outer

1	3	4	7	2	9	2	2	4	6	1	7
8	6	5	2	7	9	7	7	5	3	8	2

Fig 3b
**Showing the semi-completed construction
or outline for the Phi Code 2 Pairs of 9ness.
The Order of Plotting the 12 Pairs is geared from
starting from the Centre and moving Outwards.**

| 2 | 8 | ε | S | L | L | ϖ | L | ζ | S | 9 | 8 |
| L | I | 9 | ϖ | ζ | ζ | ϖ | ζ | L | ϖ | ε | I |

Fig 3c
Showing an "Isolation" from the semi-completed construction or outline for the multi-Dimensional Power of Phi's 12 Pairs of 9ness aka Phi Code 2.
The Order of Plotting the 12 Pairs is geared from starting from the Centre and moving Outwards.
(Just playing with the design before fully completing it!).
nb: The full black circular rim is the Double 9 Pair.

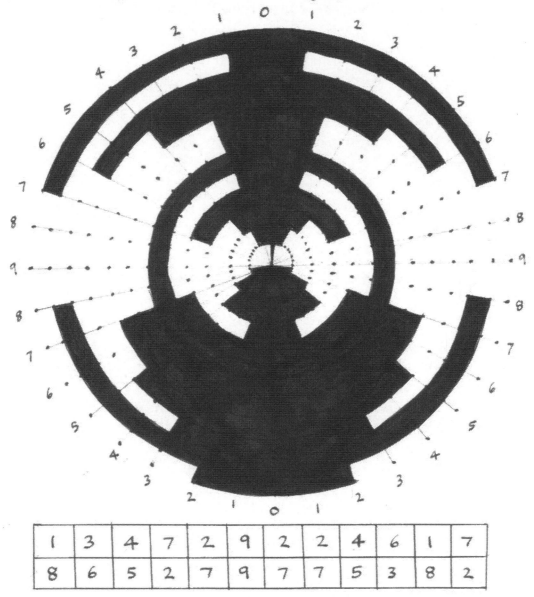

JAIN MATHEMAGICS WORKSHEET.
GRID / TEMPLATE for PLOTTING the
12 PAIRS of 9ness. (Using 10° radials)

1	3	4	7	2	9	2	2	4	6	1	7
8	6	5	2	7	9	7	7	5	3	8	2

Fig 3d
Showing the completed construction or outline
for the multi-Dimensional Power of Phi's 12 Pairs of 9ness, aka Phi
Code 2. The Order of Plotting the 12 Pairs is geared by starting
from the Centre and moving Outwards.
The central double 9 Pair (9,9) is the darkened ring segment
in the middle of the mandala.

PLOTTING THE PAIRS OF PC2 BY MOVING
FROM THE OUTER RIM AND TOWARDS THE CENTRE

The last 4 diagrams of Figs 3a, 3b, 3c and 3d showed the succession of patterns where the order was moving from the Centre towards the Outer Rim.
Now we experiment by plotting the Pairs of the Phi Code 2 by moving from the Outer Rim to the Centre as shown in Figs 4a, 4b and 4c.

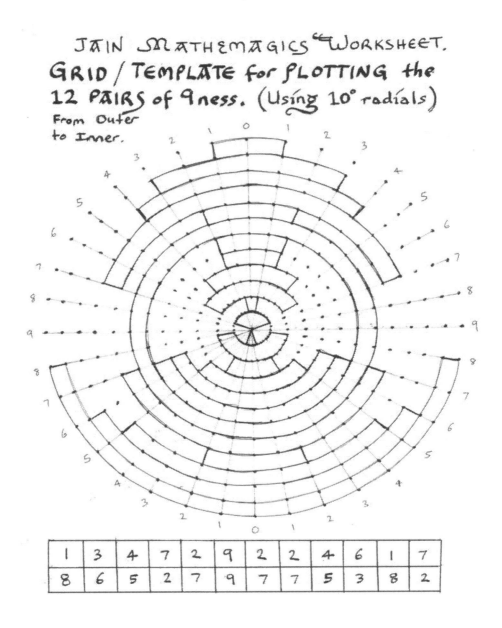

1	3	4	7	2	9	2	2	4	6	1	7
8	6	5	2	7	9	7	7	5	3	8	2

Fig 4a
Showing the semi-completed construction or outline
for the 12 Pairs of 9ness in the multi-Dimensional Powers of Phi,
aka Phi Code 2. The Order of Plotting the 12 Pairs is geared
by starting from the Outer Rim and moving to the Centre.

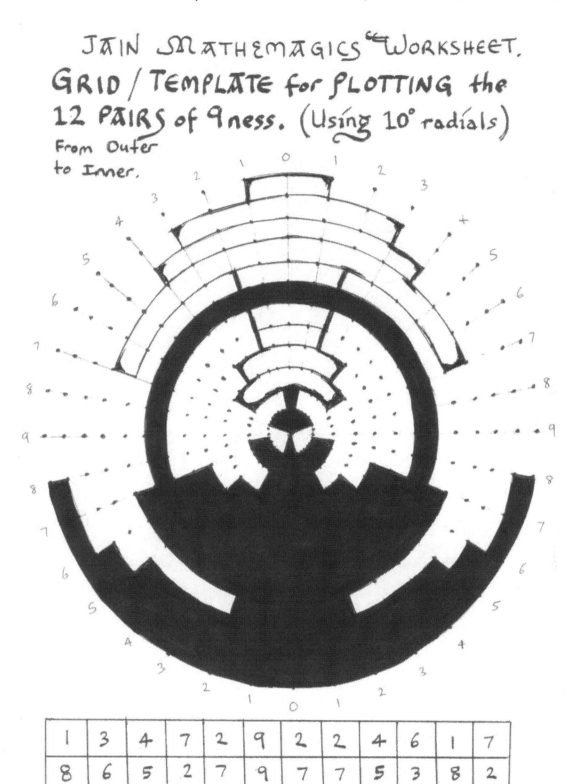

JAIN MATHEMAGICS "WORKSHEET.
GRID / TEMPLATE for PLOTTING the
12 PAIRS of 9ness. (Using 10° radials)
From Outer
to Inner.

1	3	4	7	2	9	2	2	4	6	1	7
8	6	5	2	7	9	7	7	5	3	8	2

Fig 4b
Showing an Isolation or segment from the outline
for the multi-Dimensional Power of Phi's 12 Pairs of 9ness,
aka Phi Code 2. The Order of Plotting the 12 Pairs is geared
by starting from the Outer Rim and moving to the Centre.

JAIN MATHEMAGICS WORKSHEET.
GRID / TEMPLATE for PLOTTING the
12 PAIRS of 9ness. (Using 10° radials)

1	3	4	7	2	9	2	2	4	6	1	7
8	6	5	2	7	9	7	7	5	3	8	2

Fig 4c
Showing the completed PC2 construction or outline
for the multi-Dimensional Power of Phi's 12 Pairs of 9ness.
The Order of Plotting the 12 Pairs is geared by starting
from the Outer Rim and moving to the Centre.
The central double 9 Pair (9,9) is the darkened
full ring segment in the middle of the mandala.

PHI CODE 2
VOLTAGE DIFFERENCES OF THE PAIRS
+
The PHI – PRIME COMNNECTION

Here is Phi Code 2 again in it's 2x12 rectangular array showing the 12 Pairs
The following data on this page, is just for the record. (I give it as an example
of creative exploration of these codes, questing for symmetry).

1	3	4	7	2	9	2	2	4	6	1	7
8	6	5	2	7	9	7	7	5	3	8	2

Fig 1c

Powers Of Phi aka POP2 aka PC2 (Phi Code 2) in 2x12 Array

Let us let examine the differences between the 12 Pairs of 9, without considering
any negative numbers, as in the first pair example (1 and 8), it can be read as
(1 minus 8 = minus 7) or as (8 minus 1 = 7). We select the latter method of
whole positive numbers. In a sense, it is examining the difference (diff) in
magnitude or voltage of the pairs.

The 12 Pairs are expressed like this:
(1,8) – (3,6) – (4,5) – (7,2) – (2,7) – (9,9) – (2,7) – (2,7) – (4,5) – (6,3) – (1,8) – (7,2)
or put in a tabled form when we subtract the smallest number in the Pair from
the largest number:

First Set of 12 Numbers											
1	3	4	7	2	9	2	2	4	6	1	7
Second Set of 12 Numbers											
8	6	5	2	7	9	7	7	5	3	8	2

Fig 1d

Numerical Differences or "Voltages" between the 12 Pairs of the Powers Of Phi

There appears another palindromic sequence, based on Prime Numbers, in the
first 11 of the 12 Pairs.

Now let us list the differences between each Pair:

7 – 3 – 1 – 5 – 5 – 0 – 5 – 5 – 1 – 3 – 7 – (5)

The final digit (5) is put in parentheses as it is not part of the palindromic sequence. This solution is a neat possible candidate for a Phi / Prime Connection!

This ends this Phi Prime Connection, and we now return to the circular worksheets coming up where we graph or plot these Pair Differences.

These differences act like a force between the extremes of the Pair, acting like an electrical voltage or a tension that exists in it's very nature. Yet, as we will see, there is an exquisite order, a harmony or an innate balance between all of this apparent random-looking chaos of the phi codes.

Before we shade in or blacken the Pair differences, I will first outline or mark in bold the actual Pairs, in Fig 5b so we can get an overall view of this cryptic cosmic spider-web.

Also, to mark these Pairs, we assume that all counting begins from the center point, thus when we mark any pair like (1,8) we count from the centre and mark the first and eighth concentric circles.

You will see in Fig 5b that the 12 Pairs have been written on the outer rim of the 9th circle because that is the specific information that will be plotted in that slice of the pie being a $1/12^{th}$ segment.

Regarding the position where to start plotting the 12 Pairs on the Circle, the obvious or most conventional starting point is to follow the motions of the clock, thus the first pair in Phi Code 1 being (1,8) will be placed at the 1:00 o'clock position, then continue clockwise to plot the 2nd pair (3,6) etc.

Also Fig 5b is merely a halfway design, that it, it is not completed until Fig 5c. Sometimes by merely drawing outlines of the arcs, stopping and observing your work at the halfway marks can lead to inspiration or reflection. It's like taking a deep breath, a reflective pause, a moment to inspect what is being created, before it is created; out of the depths of our deep subconscious worlds. It is an emphasis to raise or praise and periscope your head upon the new landmarks, to open more your consciousness and drink in the surrounding environs, as if landing on the moon for the first time; or like a cat playing with it's captured prey, it's time to look at the new breed of mice in your net. What have we here? you the detective of patterns. What is the form of this gift of god that I am on the verge of eating, devouring, how pretty are your fine microscopic capillaries running along those shimmering wings says the lizard to the dragonfly in it's mouth, yet what I eat or capture I become, for it is I and I am it. Suddenly in this mathematical Oneness, there is no master or slave or tyrant, no predator or victim. The apparent duality of the Pairs of 9, all these opposing codes were necessary to realize this Unity Consciousness, the ability to **Uni-Phi**.

PLOTTING THE 12 PAIRS OF PC2
INTO THE CIRCLE DIVIDED INTO 108 SEGMENTS

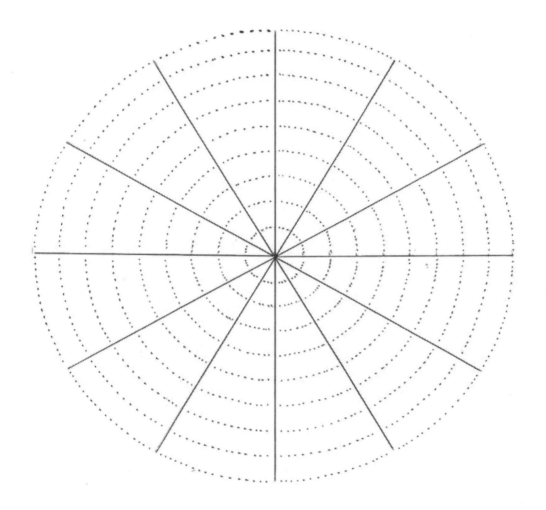

Jain Mathemagics Worksheet
The CIRCLE DIVIDED
Into 108 Segments

(Composed of 12 RADIALS and
9 CONCENTRIC CIRCLES).

Fig 5a
The Circle Divided into 108 Segments
composed of 12 Radials and 9 Concentric Circles
(typical Worksheet for the Jain Mathemagics Curriculum for The Global School).

Jain Mathemagics Worksheet
The CIRCLE DIVIDED
Into   108 Segments

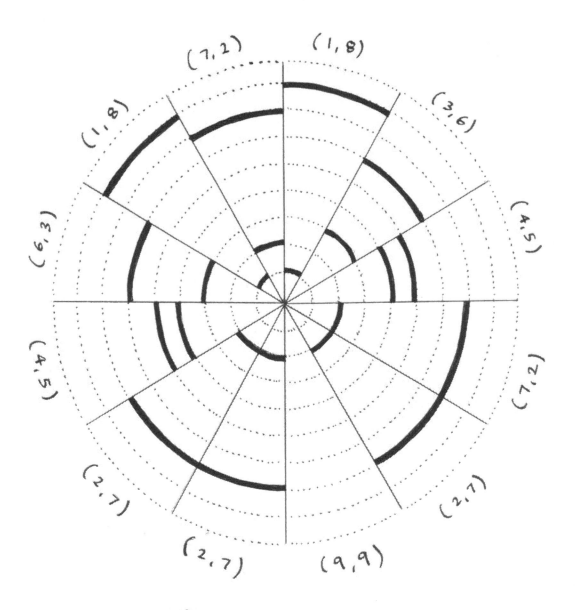

(Composed of 12 RADIALS and
9 CONCENTRIC CIRCLES).

Fig 5b
The halfway mark or outlines for PHI CODE 2
plugged internally into the Circle divided into 108 Segments.
The Bolded Lines or Arcs represent the numerical difference
between the numbers of the 12 Pairs.

Jain Mathemagics Worksheet
The CIRCLE DIVIDED
Into 108 Segments~

Pairs for the
Powers of Phi.

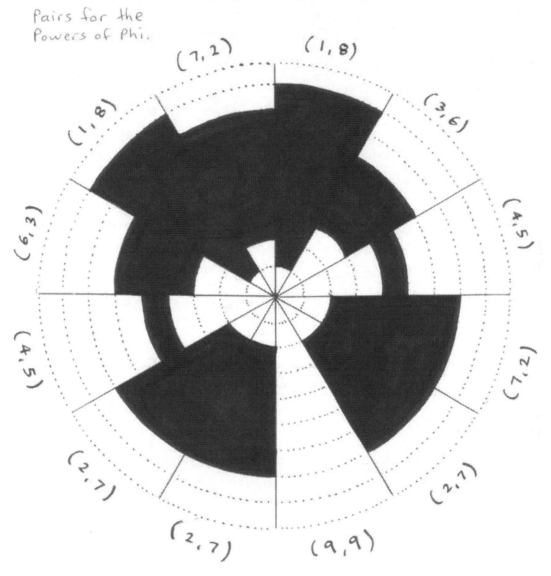

(Composed of 12 RADIALS and
9 CONCENTRIC CIRCLES).

Fig 5c
PHI CODE 2 Plugged internally into
the Circle divided into 108 Segments.
The completed shaded areas represent the numerical
difference between the numbers of the 12 Pairs.

COMPARISON OF THE FIRST 2 PHI CODES: BOTH ARE GEOMETRICALLY BALANCED

Did you notice that both these circular yantra (Phi Code 1 and Phi Code 2 discs) have a distinct balance regarding their Pairs.

To see this clearly let us take this completed Phi Code 2 pattern shown in Fig 5c and compare it to the pattern of Phi Code 1 drawn in the previous book (call it Fig 6a here), and tilt them around so as to align the (9,9) Pair in the north or topmost position, like the clock's position for exact midday or zenith point.

The following diagrams Figs 6a and 6b have been cropped and tilted from previous diagrams. This will show both Phi Code 1 and Phi Code 2 on the same page for our better observation and scrutiny.

Regarding Phi Code 1, as shown here as Fig 6a, scan your eyes around the pivotal northern pair of (9,9) and observe that the nearest Pairs surrounding it are (8,1) and (1,8) which have the same difference or voltage. Then the next pairs equidistant from the central (9,9) pair are (1,8) and (1,8), then (7,2) and (2,7), then (3,6) and (3,6), then (4,5) and (5,4) leaving at the base of the diagram the sole pair (1,8).

What do you notice?

One theme of the Jain 108 Mathemagics Curriculum is to get the student to "discover" mathematics and geometries. This is supported by converting numbers into art. Now we derive learning from mere observation of this visual data. It is that simple.

The answer is that it is perfectly balanced along the vertical axis, that is if you folded the disc in half along this vertical axis the shaded areas would perfect align meaning that each half is a mirror-image of the other half. Great idea for a circuit board where electrons are taught to flow with intelligence and obeying the Laws of Nature.

Then have a look at the reoriented Fig 6b of PC2 and observe the differences of the pairs on either side of the topmost (9,9) pair. Here are the 12 pairs again:

(1,8) – (3,6) – (4,5) – **(7,2)** – **(2,7)** – (9,9) – **(2,7)** – **(2,7)** – (4,5) – (6,3) – (1,8) – (7,2).

I have highlighted in bold the two set of pairs that sandwich the middle (9,9,) pair, for you to recognize that the differences of "5" are the same.

Our job, as stated by Viktor Schauberger (1885-1958) is to "Copy and Comprehend Nature". (Viktor, in the passion of studying how his Austrian creeks flowed, succeeded in becoming the Master of the Water Element. So wanted was he by the Men In Black plutocracy, that Hitler apparently kidnapped him to build up his developing secret UFO fleet, and thus Viktor applied the same genius and became the Master of the Air Element. None of the technology has been permitted to become visible to the world for reasons of control, and Viktor died a sad man that his Pure Intent was applied towards selfish military consciousness; that is why it could not succeed as the energies of manipulation are a lower or denser frequency than what Love is).

Fig 6a indicates that the significant pair surrounding the topmost (9,9) pair is the (1,8) or (8,1) pair.
Fig 6b indicates that the significant pair surrounding the topmost (9,9) pair is the (2,7) or (7,2) pair.

[With this partial knowledge of conjugal systems or clue, I could therefore predict that there exists another or third 108 Phi Code whose significant pairs surrounding the topmost (9,9) pair is the (4,5) or (5,4) pairs].

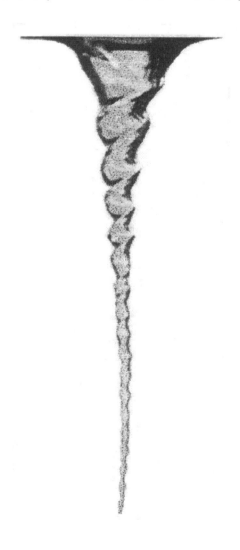

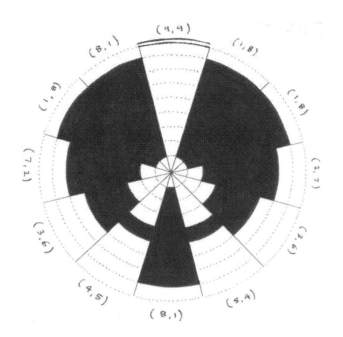

Fig 6a
Phi Code 1's significant pair (9,9) aligned to the North Position.
The entire diagram displays "Mirror-Imaging" in the North/South
vertical axis, ie: can fold over itself symmetrically.

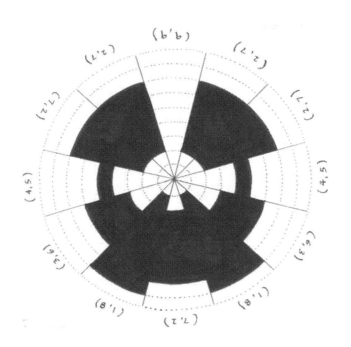

Fig 6b
(reoriented from Fig 5c)
Phi Code 2's significant pair (9,9) aligned to the North Position.
The entire diagram displays "Mirror-Imaging" in the North/South vertical axis,
ie: can fold over itself symmetrically.

PLOTTING PHI CODE 2
UPON THE 9 POINT CIRCLE

Jain Mathemagics Worksheet
For the plotting of the 24 Repeating Powers Of Phi
Upon the 9 point circle.

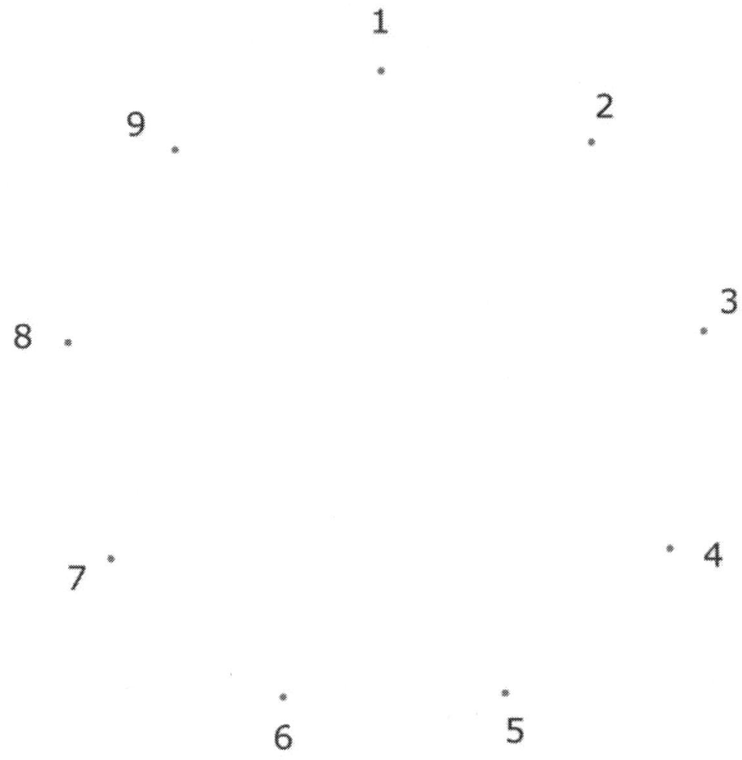

1

9

2

8

3

7

4

6   5

The Circle Of 9 Dots, Numbered from 1 to 9

Fig 7

Upon the 9 Point Circle, Join The Dots from
1 to 3 to 4 to 7 to 2 to 9 etc to the last digit 2.

1 – 3 – 4 – 7 – 2 – 9 – 2 – 2 – 4 – 6 – 1 – 7
8 – 6 – 5 – 2 – 7 – 9 – 7 – 7 – 5 – 3 – 8 – 2

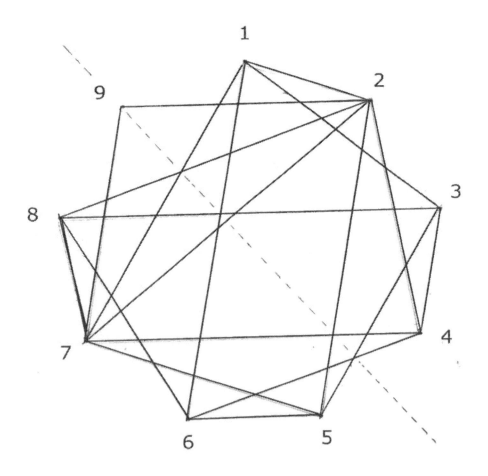

Fig 8

Jain's Powers Of Phi Code 108
plotted upon the 9 point circle, reveals mirror-imaged symmetry!

Make sure that when you have joined the last or 24th number, that you close the circuit by joining the Alpha & Omega ie: join the last number "2" back to the first number "1" otherwise the symmetry or mirror-imaging will be broken.

When the 24 single digits are plotted on the 9 Point Circle, an interesting pattern appears. There appears an obvious symmetry around the axis that passes diametrically through the line touching the Number 9 and the opposing midpoint between 4 and 5, call it the "9 / 4.5 axis". That means if you were to fold this design in half on paper along this "9 / 4.5 axis", it would superimpose upon itself.

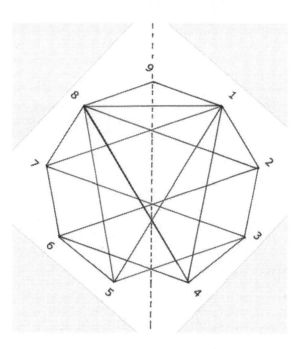

Phi Code 1 on the 9 Point Circle

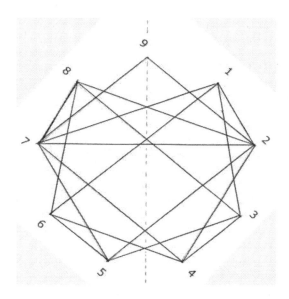

Phi Code 2 on the 9 Point Circle

Fig 9
The TWO (of the 3) POSSIBLE PHI CODES 108
on the 9 POINT CIRCLE.
A visual examination of
Phi Code 1 plotted upon the 9 Point Circle and
Phi Code 2 plotted upon the 9 Point Circle
merely for the possibility of looking for similarities or differences.

ON THE HARMONIC OF 216
& THE MYSTICAL SQUARING OF THE CIRLCE

Just to show you how nerds like me spend their time, engrossed in the Phi Code Mysteries, I would look at the proportion of the shaded area to the non-shaded area and check if any harmonically important numbers appear.

I will arrive at a "**Harmonic of 216**" in a strange way, which is important to mathematicians and physicists, but not interesting for the average reader, so you can dismiss this page and move to the next. The following is merely for the record, a lot of calculations can happen and be discarded, looking for these mathematical gems. Like a cartoon, where piles of screwed up paper are being tossed into the waste paper bin!

We know that the circle has 108 segments (Fig 5a). It is easy to count the shaded areas, as they are merely the differences between the pairs.

As shown before, **Phi Code 1** consists of the following 12 Pairs represented like this:

(1,8) – (1,8) – (2,7) – (3,6) – (5,4) – (8,1) –
(4,5) – (3,6) – (7,2) – (1,8) – (8,1) – (9,9).

Now let us list the differences between each Pair:

7-7-5-3-1-7-1-3-5-7-7-0

What is the sum of these 12 numbers?

7+7+5+3+1+7+1+3+5+7+7+0 = 53

We can conclude that **the shaded area of Phi Code 1 = 53**

Let us now look at **Phi Code 2** which consists of the following 12 Pairs represented like this:

(1,8) – (3,6) – (4,5) – (7,2) – (2,7) – (9,9) –
(2,7) – (2,7) – (4,5) – (6,3) – (1,8) – (7,2).

Now let us list the differences between each Pair:

7-3-1-5-5-0-5-5-1-3-7-5

What is the sum of these 12 numbers?

7+3+1+5+5+0+5+5+1+3+7+5 = 47

We can conclude that **the shaded area of Phi Code 2 = 47**

Let us relate these two numbers to the 108 total of segments and work out the following possible calculations of division:

Phi Code 1 proportion of shaded area is either :

$108 \div 53 = 2.037735849$ or
$53 \div 108 = .49\ 074\ 074\ 074$

Phi Code 2 proportion of shaded area is either :
$108 \div 47 = 2.29787234$
$47 \div 108 = .435185185$ or $.435\underline{185}...$

None of these 4 number proportions ring any bells so we can try something else. All that I can see is that the two proportion numbers 53 and 47 have a sum of **100** which is inviting, suggesting that the combined 2 lots of 108 segments will have a sum of 216, and this divided by 100 is 2.16. Now bells start to ring!

$216 \div 100 = \mathbf{2.16}$
$100 \div 216 = .4\ 629\ 629\ 629$

(in maths, the simplified way to write ".4 629 629 629..." is to express it as: ".4$\underline{629}$... " where the underlined section of "629" repeats forever, in Base 10 only, but an underline in not used, mathematicians put a small dot over the 6 and the 9 to imply that the three digits of "629" actually repeat forever. The forever bit is symbolized by the 3 trailing dots "...".

The 2 lots of 108 segments is like having both discs printed on clear plastic and either overlaid/superimposed or joined back to back. Either way, there are 216 segments to be divided by the 100 shaded areas giving the proportion of 2.16. According to **Bruce Cathie**, the NZ air pilot who developed the world wide grid based on ufo sightings, has a developed a 3-Dimensional form of angular mathematics of harmonics where all zeroes and decimal points are deleted.
eg: the **Harmonic of Light** is based on the **Reciprocal of 144** which is 1 ÷ 144 or $1/144 = .00694444444...$repeater (keeps going forever with the 4s and is pronounced as "point zero zero six nine four repeater").
He rounds off the "4 repeater" to a 5 and gets .00695.
He is only interested in whole integers so both zeroes are taken away and so is the decimal point. What is left is the **Harmonic of 695**. (He has written a whole book just on this lost and advanced vortex mathematics. His work is equally as important as Viktor Schauberger mentionned before).
Thus in our case, the two Phi Code discs joined back to back have a shaded area proportional to 2.16 and is recorded here as the **Harmonic of 216**.

So, as an early conclusion, I could summarize that my life's work and research on the 2 possible Phi Codes fit snuggly onto a double sided coin. They are conjugal or married or related to one another. They fit together most harmonically ringing a frequency based on the Harmonic of 216 being double 108.

I could keep going down this rabbit hole and examine more differences in the following numbers:

Phi Code 1 proportion of shaded area is 53/108 = .49 074 074

Phi Code 2 proportion of shaded area is 47/108 = .435185185

The difference between .49<u>074</u>... and .435<u>185</u>... is
.055555555555555...
Would Bruce Cathie call this Harmonic 5 or Harmonic 55 or Harmonic 555 etc.?
If he simplified the decimal by rounding off the repeaters as he did in the reciprocal of 144 example above, he would have .05 Repeater expressed as .056 which becomes **Harmonic 56.**

This grand realization of the **all-pervading Harmonic of 216** may not mean much to you but in the world of harmonic mathematics (or cycles per second, or Hertz frequency), it is an important link.

eg: how do we determine the **Harmonic of Time?**
Since we are interested in the **Physics of Time Bending** and Astral Travelling, let us look at **how many seconds there are in a day!**
60 seconds in a minute
60 minutes in an hour
24 hours in a day.
Thus the number of seconds in a day are: 60 x 60 x 24 = 86,400.
Cathie would drop the zeroes and conclude that the Harmonic of Time is **864.**
(and if you measured the **diameter of the sun** it is 864,000 miles, drop the zeroes and you get **864 Harmonic**).
Now how does this relate to our Phi Code Harmonic 216?
Create a binary code of 27, which means start with 27 then keep doubling the answer, like this:

27 – 54 – 108 – **216** – 432 – **864** – **1728** – **3456** etc

all of which are very important or anointed numbers.

So you can see from the "**27 Binary Code**" that **216** is a factor of the **864**. Why did we start doubling with the number 27?

This was Pythagoras' favourite number, a window into the mystery of the universe. Cathie says that his system of hours in a day is based on 27 not 24, to make the magic work. When the atomic bomb was dropped on Nagasaki, not only did the drop have to happen onto a node or intersection point on the geometric grid around the earth, but the maths was based on 27 hours in a day!

Now there is nothing wrong with 24 and 27, actually they are well suited. What is the proportion of 24 to 27. Both numbers divide by 3 giving us an 8:9 proportion (which is the grid required to "Square The Circle").

There is a very special association with 9 and 8, in the sense that if you have an 8x8 grid of 64 squares like the chessboard or graph paper, and you wanted to "Square The Circle", (which symbolically makes Heaven and Earth as One or Equal), you need to construct a 9x9 =81 grid of squares around the 8x8, and draw a circle from the two common centres to make the circumference of the 8x8 circle to be equal to the perimeter of the 8x8 square.

There are two examples of the circle's quadrature shown in Figs 10a and Fig 10b.

That is 9, and only 9 can mystically square the circle, and to square the circle, one has to increase the radius of the unit circle from 1 unit to 1.272... which is the square root of the Golden Mean 1.618033..., that is, only Phi, dancing with 9 can make the magic of the worlds open up. **Only the Square Root of Phi makes Heaven and Earth Equal**.

(I would like to write a separate book just on this topic, The Squaring of the Circle. In my Jain Mathemagics Mystery School, The Mystical Squaring of the Circle constitutes a day of teaching, as would other related topics like the Vesica Piscis, the Pyramids, the Pentacle, the 5 Platonic Solids, the 13 Archimedean Solids etc).

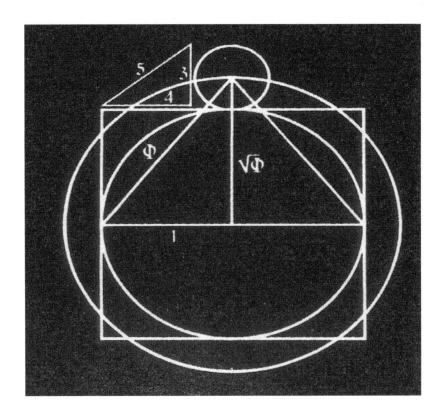

Fig 10a
The Mystical Squaring of the Circle,
and Pyramid Harmonics of Gizeh,
containing also the Phi Ratio (1:1.618033...),
the Square Root of Phi (1.272...),
and the 345 Pythagorean Triangle ($3^2 + 4^2 = 5^2$).

In Fig 10b, observe the square ABCD below.

It has an apothem (a line that is at right-angles) OV of 1 unit.

That means that the length of each side of the square are 2 unit's each, giving the perimeter of the square to be 8 unit's. We want to examine what the corresponding circle having a circumference of 8 unit's would like!

(It is the circle that just cut inside of the 4 corners, touching F and E).

There is a straight line going through **LOVE**. To know how to square the circle requires a process of elongating the apothem OV to the new radius of OE. It is only a slight increase, but specifically, by extrapolating OV to OE, ie: when we make OE = 1.272... we then successfully **Square Our Circle** or Circle Our Square.

They are now both equal.

This value of 1.272... is the **square root of Phi**, that is, what number multiplied by itself gives 1.618...,

ie: 1.272... x 1.272... = 1.618...

I am not giving all the mathematics on how I derived this value of 1.272... just trust that it is true.

Only Phi, the Golden Mean, the Divine Proportion, can mystically Square the Circle!

(In the sequel to this book, Book of Phi, Volume 7, you will learn, that only Phi can determine the True Value of Pi = 3.144...) which utilizes this ancient knowledge of the Phi Code and introduces us to another important subject on The ART of **INTUITIVE MATHEMATICS.**

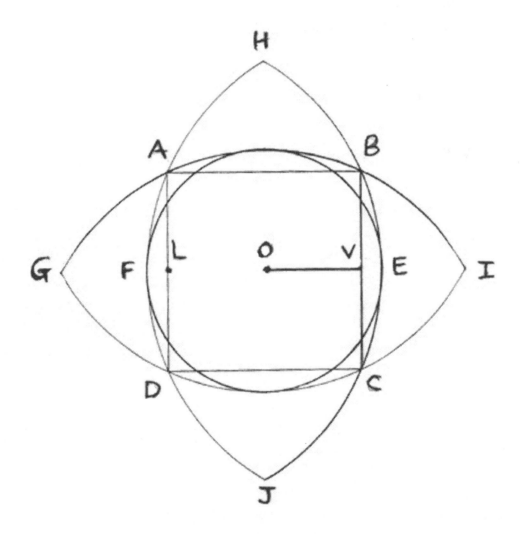

Fig 10b
The Mystical Squaring of the Circle
showing the formation of L-O-V-E

A NEW MODEL: The ART of HOW to UNI-PHI

At this stage, all you need to understand is that **You are the Phi Ratio**, which is nothing more than the sacred place where the elbow bends; you have memory and innate knowledge of everything printed not only in this book but all books, for you are The Book of Life. **You are Phi Micro internalized in your very DNA and Phi Macro externalized in the distances of the planets from the Sun**, so don't worry about any of the numbers or algebraic musings, just remember the Love.

(The **Heart Math Institute** can scientifically verify that when you feel real Love or Compassion, it can be measured, using Harmonics of Phi 1.618033. This is the purpose of this book, to bridge the metaphysics of what I am on about, the Phi Mysteries, with the physics of the scientific world).

There is thus no separation. All that we can do now in these changing and politically unstable times, is to give our children the best education possible, and the ultimate is to align our distinguished **Vortex Mathematics** with the dazzling efficiency of the sunflower (21:34 coding) and or the pine cone (8:13 coding).

As we approach and metamorphose into the imminent and unavoidable One World Government, which does not necessarily have to be evil, you can spell "evil" backwards, we can perceive it as a positive pathway. We will need our children to design a new **One World Flag**. My recommendation would be to have this emblem based on the **21:34 counter-rotating spirals of the SunFlower floret**, shown below in Fig 11 (notice that 21 is a Fibonacci Number, and is specific to the number of spirals depicted). This is not only the true meaning of **Flower Power**, it takes this knowledge to the highest plateau in that it is simple, easy to understand, easy to replicate and teach, and is the principle or **PhiLosoPhi** of how Schauberger's ufo crafts operated.

Just like a gently flowing creek in the rainforest, Spin is Life; Phi's cascading ratios allows the spin to enter the equation. Keep on spinning and dancing, this will improve your astral hygiene. Eat more live raw foods. Above all, to bring real change into the world, as a spiritual warrior now armed with this knowledge, you need to have lots of spin which is lots of good strong Health. Make time for daily physical exercise and meditation.

This is called The **Art of How to SanctiPhi**.

This is called **The Art of How to Uni-Phi**.

This is really knowing how to **give Gratitude**.

You are now pleasantly **Imbued by Phi.**
This we call **Engrailed**, for you are the fractal Cup within the Cup.

Fig 11
Sunflower Emblem for the New One World Flag.
(Image taken from: Robert Dixon's work referenced in
"Spiral Symmetry" editors Istvan Hargittai and Clifford A. Pickover)

I pray that these two revealed Phi Codes will accelerate the awakening of our peoples and gear our guiding schools towards the **Fibonaccization** of the entire world: One World, One Currency, One Language, One Train Track, One Flag and of course One Mathematics.

Fig 12

The 5 Psycho-Active Disks
generated from this Article,
than can be used as
pocket-sized talismans!

This concludes this section.

~ CHAPTER 2 ~

PHI CODE 2
AS 3 X 8 & 4 X 6 MATRICES
REVEALING ANCIENT
SOLFEGGIO SCALES

This Chapter 2 Includes:

- Examination Of Alternate Pairs In Phi Code 2 aka Lucas Sequence
- Phi Code 2 as a 3x8 Matrix
- Phi Code 2 as a 4x6 Matrix
- Comparison of the Two Phi Codes Analyzing their 12 Pairs of 9ness
- Practical Application of the 108 Phi Codes.

PHI CODE 2
aka PC (1,3,4)
aka POWERS OF PHI 108 CODE
aka PHI CODE " 108+9"
aka LUCAS SEQUENCE
and
EXPRESSED as 3 x 8 and 4 x 6 MATRICES
Or RECTANGULAR ARRAYS

As explained previously, there are 3 distinct Phi Codes of 108.

We can be more precise and say that there exist 3 Primal Phi Codes that sum to 108 and that these 3 generate 72 possible permutations. This fact regarding the 72 various permutations will be revealed in the next book: THE BOOK OF PHI, volume 7, sub-titled: The 3 Phi Codes.

It will show how these 72 strings of Digitally Compressed 24 Repeating Patterns can be simplified or rewritten as Triplets. It appears to be a connection with the ancient 72 Angelic Names or Names of God...

We just revealed that both the first one PC1 (which is the basic compression of the Living Mathematics of Nature, the Fibonacci Sequence), and PC2 (based on the Powers of Phi) both have a sum of 108 or 12 Pairs of 9, but since one of these Pairs is really a double 9, the true or legitimate sum is 108+9 and the Phi Code is not just Phi Code 108 but really:

Phi Code 108+9 = 108 – 9 – 108 – 9 – 108 – 9 – 108 – 9 etc

whose Sum or Sigma $\sum$ = 117.

EXAMINATION OF ALTERNATE PAIRS IN PHI CODE 2 aka LUCAS SEQUENCE

PHI CODE 2: POWERS OF PHI / LUCAS NUMBERS																							
1³	4⁷	2⁹	2²	4⁶	1⁷	8⁶	5²	7⁹	7⁷	5³	8²

Fig 1

The Powers of Phi 24 Repeating Code or Pattern is identical to
the Lucas Numbers Sequence revered by stock-marketeering experts.

Have a look at the Alternate Pairs in Fig 1 above, that is, every second number:

1, 3, 4, 7, 2, 9, 2, 2, 4, 6, 1, 7, 8, 6, 5, 2, 7, 9, 7, 7, 5, 3, 8, 2

1 – 4 – 2 – 2 – 4 – 1 – 8 – 5 – 7 – 7 – 5 – 8

Notice that the outer Pairs haves sums of 9.

Now observing the remaining alternate Numbers:

1, 3, 4, 7, 2, 9, 2, 2, 4, 6, 1, 7, 8, 6, 5, 2, 7, 9, 7, 7, 5, 3, 8, 2

3 – 7 – 9 – 2 – 6 – 7 – 6 – 2 – 9 – 7 – 3 – 2

which is palindromic, literally "running backwards", except for the last digit "2".

1	3	4	7	2	9	2	2	4	6	1	7	8	6	5	2	7	9	7	7	5	3	8	2

Fig 2

Highlighting the Alternate Numbers in Phi Code 2

This was to merely to illustrate how there exist patterns within patterns, the task is knowing intuitively which door to enter into the labyrinth.

Let us turn our attention into converting this linear row of 1x24 to the 3x8 and 4x6 configurations.

(Art of Jain, 1996)

PHI CODE 2 as a 3x8 MATRIX

THE DIGITALLY COMPRESSED 24 REPEATING PATTERN of PHI CODE 2 EXPRESSED as a TRINITIZED MATRIX or RECTANGULAR ARRAY of 3x8

1	3	4	7	2	9	2	2
4	6	1	7	8	6	5	2
7	9	7	7	5	3	8	2

Fig 3
3x8 Rectangular Array of Phi Code 2
showing repetition in the 4th and 8th columns
of 777 and 222, highlighted & the remaining columns
constitute the ancient Solfeggio Triplet Scales.

Of interest here are the columns that do not have **rep digits** (ie: repeating digits above like 777 and 222). All these columns appear in the table of 18 possible Solfeggio Scale Triplets, which will be discussed in full in the next book on Phi, volume 7: The 3 Phi Codes. The Triplets emerge from the common phone pad of 9 numbers in a 3x3 square and we take the 3 rows of 1-4-7, 2-5-8 and 3-6-9 and can rearrange these numbers in any 6 possible ways, eg 147 can be rearranged as 417 or 714 etc and these **anagrams** act as frequencies or Hertz (cycles per second).

PHI CODE 2 as a 4x6 MATRIX

Let us express the same Phi Code 2 or Powers of Phi, into the 4x6 Frame.

1	3	4	7	2	9
2	2	4	6	1	7
8	6	5	2	7	9
7	7	5	3	8	2

Fig 4
4x6 Rectangular Array of Phi Code 2
showing 5 columns having sums of 18 and the final column summing 27.

(Art of Jain, 1997)

COMPARISON of the first TWO PHI CODES, Analyzing their 12 PAIRS of 9NESS

Phi Code 1:

1	1	2	3	5	8	4	3	7	1	8	9
8	8	7	6	4	1	5	6	2	8	1	9

Phi Code 2:

1	3	4	7	2	9	2	2	4	6	1	7
8	6	5	2	7	9	7	7	5	3	8	2

Fig 5
Comparison of the first two Phi 108 Codes
Specifically analyzing the placement
of the Double 9 Bonds or Pairs of 9

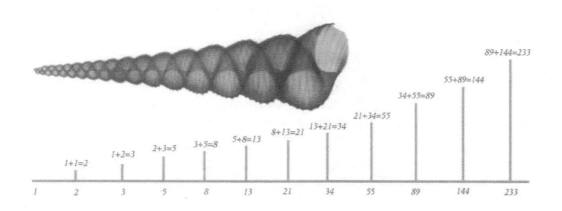

Fig 6
Seashell in it's elongated form represents closely
the Jacob's Laddering of the Powers Of Phi,
Symbolic of the multi-dimensional caduceus logo.

PRACTICAL APPLICATION OF THE 108 PHI CODES

These sequences can also be creatively applied to musical scales and colour frequencies etc. to assist in the healing of the body, mind and spirit, and to raise the consciousness of the Planet.

Here are some various activities and crafts that can be designed to embed this knowledge into the creative arts, and ultimately into our Hearts.

• **Make a Fashion Belt:**
I would suggest to have 24 small Phi Ratioed Rectangles that are to be coloured in from a palette of **9 favourite colours**, so that the strict structure of the above sequences are obeyed by ascribing say
1 = Red, 2 = Orange, 3 = Yellow, 4 =Green, 5 = Blue, 6 = Indigo,
7 = Violet, 8 = Pink, 9 = Rose

• **Make a Fashion Necklace** or a monk's Mala Beads for chanting.
Again, specify 9 colours for the single 9 digits in the 24 repeating code, if the size of the beads are all the same size and shape.
If you like, you can use **9 different shapes** of beads to translate this code into a physical form.

• **Make a Floor Tiling** based on the 1x24 or 2x12 or 3x8 or 4x6 Frames. Again, you can use **9 colours**, but since this is an experiment in consciousness, where there are no rules, and all possibilities, you could use one colour throughout but **having 9 different textures or shadings**.

• **Make Phi Code Music** based on the selection of 9 different and favourite notes that can be selected from a child's Xylophone. Instead of 9 individual notes which would give a linear or monotonous feeling to the music, you could select say 9 distinct chords.
You could look at the 12 Pairs of 9 and use these 2 patterns, to combine 2 chords at a time to complete one cycle of the 2x12 frame.
Or, regarding the 4x6 frames, you could take 4 notes or 4 chords at a time using 4 people or musicians in the band to translate the numbers into music.

• **Do you have your own original suggestions that can translate the 108 Phi Codes** into this earthly realm? literally to bring down Heaven into the duality of Earth; but if you understand Unity Consciousness, that is, how to UNI-

PHI, there is no above or below, no heaven or earth, only Holo-Luminous interconnectedness and fractality as we begin this process of **Fibonaccization of the Human Species**, toroidally embedding this self-similar, infinitely recursive trinitized Mathematics of the Soul, into our Heart, our EarthHeart beat of 108 Hertz, cycles per second.

Blessings from Jain 108

DID YOU KNOW?
That Phi is really based on a Trinity!

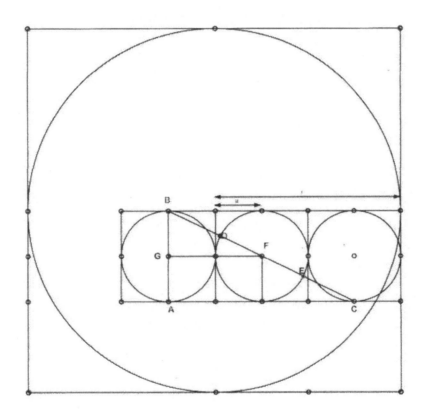

Fig 7
Phi is based on the TRINTIY:
Geometric derivation of the Phi Ratio (being BE / GF)
using 3 smaller circles within the larger circle.
This is also the basis for the Proof of Phi derived from Pi (the squared circle,
where the large square is divided into 16 smaller squares).

(This rare and beautiful diagram is inspired from Bengt Erik Erlandsen,
taken from http://GoldenNumber.net/PhiFormulaGeometry.htm).

~ CHAPTER 3 ~

POWERS OF PHI PROVED

Demonstrated to Repeat Correctly
Every 24th Power
Using 77 Decimal Places
(Not Using 9 Decimal Places that falters)

by

Jain 108

9th / 9 / 1999

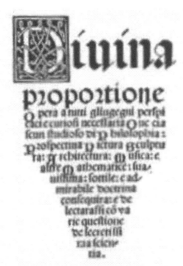

(front cover of De Divina Proportione by Fra Luca Pacioli,
illustrated by Leonardo da Vinci and published in Venice in 1509).

This page includes:

- All data up to the 50th Power of Phi using Phi to 77 Decimal Places

- 2 Page summary chart showing all data up to the 50th Power of
  Phi expressed as "phi^50"

- "24 Repeating Pattern", and the "Odd, Odd, Even" Pattern

- Lucas Numbers
  1, 3, 4, 7, 2, 9, 2, 2, 4, 6, 1, 7, 8, 6, 5, 2, 7, 9, 7, 7, 5, 3, 8, 2

- Origin Of Medical Symbol: Caduceus

- All false data up to the 50th Power of Phi using Phi to 9 Decimal Places

ALL DATA UP TO THE 50TH POWER OF PHI
USING PHI TO 77 DECIMAL PLACES

The infinite Powers of Phi can best be visualized
as the increasing turns or visible rungs or incremental divisions
of this very elongated seashell and the twisting water vortex.

Here is an amazing discovery that could only be found using a calculator that had 77 decimal places. I will show you the 24 Repeating Pattern in the Powers of Phi in two versions or tables, the correct version in September 9th 1999 where I used 77 Decimal places (Using CCalc true up to 80 Decimal Places DP), and another table, the failed one in May 1999, where I used only the standard 9 decimal places on your typical calculator.

Somehow the extreme accuracy of these following numbers was the critical factor in discovering the 24 Repeating Pattern.

I think it is important to at least supply all my working out here, you can just skip these tables and accept that for the first time the Powers of Phi hold yet another 108 key, it will be known as PHI CODE 2.

I am very proud of this discovery realized just before the turn of the bi-millennium, and have waited all these years to actually publish this very rare material.

The numbers below are first establishing all the powers of Phi up to Phi to the 50th Power (ϕ^{50}), to get the correct numbers to 77 dp, then they will be all put into a table. It may appear to be doubling up the information, but I welcome any mathematician who doubts this discovery to be able to follow exactly what I have written here and have it proved by themselves.

The symbol for "power" here, also known as the exponent or index (plural = indices) is "^" thus Phi^3 means Phi to the 3rd power.

I give thanks to the internet for providing a free download of **CCalc** true up to 80 Decimal Places (80 dp).

In the mathematics below, the Lucas Number is the Power of Phi being rounded off to the nearest whole number,

eg: **phi^3 =**
4.23606797749978969640917366873127623544061835961115257242
708972454105209256377857

which is rounded off to 4 as the nearest whole integer.

Notice also that the 77 decimal places takes 2 lines of information, so to lessen space in this document I have reduced the two lines down to one, and reduced the font size after the second decimal, which also highlights the fact that 4.23 is closest to 4 and this is called the Lucas Number. Thus the same data would like this:

4.23 606797749978969640917366873127623544061835961152572427089724541052092563 7787

and since we don't need all these numbers anyway, I have shortened them so that the Lucas Number can fit on the same line.

What is a Lucas Number? It evolves from an infinite arithmetic or additive series, very similar to the Fibonacci Series which starts with 1, 1, but this sequence starts with 1, 3. The next number is the sum of these two previous ones, thus 1+3=4;

then the next number in the series 1, 3, 4 is 3+4=7;

then the next number in the series 1, 3, 4, 7 is 4+7=11 etc

Each one of these numbers just happens to approximate to the Powers of Phi.

No wonder this series is worshipped by the stock marketeers! It is based purely on Nature's Laws.

Allowing Phi to the Power of Zero = 1

• Phi^0 = 1

Lucas Number = 1

• Phi =
1.61 8033988749894848204586834365638117720309179805762862135448622705260 46281890

to 77 dp

nb: All the following values of phi from here on go to only 55 dp so the data can fit just one line rather than 2 lines, but just know that it is phi to 77dp.

Nb: Phi (with a Capital "P") represents 1.618033... though, phi (with a lower case "p") represents it's reciprocal (1 ÷ 1.618033 also expressed as 1÷ φ or 1/φ) which equals .618033...

DID YOU KNOW that Phi is the only number in the Universe where if you subtract that number's reciprocal, it equals 1 or UNITY. This is a very special quality.

LISTING OF THE INCREMENTAL 50 POWERS OF PHI

- Phi^1 (or phi^0 = 1)

1.6180339887498948482045868343656381177203091798057628621^1

Lucas Number = 1

- Phi^2

1.6180339887498948482045868343656381177203091798057628621^2

ans =   Lucas Number = 3

2.61 803398874989484820458683436563811772030917980576286213544862270526046281 88945

- Phi^3

1.6180339887498948482045868343656381177203091798057628621^3

ans =   Lucas Number = 4

4.23 6067977499789696409173668731276235440618359611525724270897245410520925637 7857

- Phi^4

1.6180339887498948482045868343656381177203091798057628621^4

ans =   Lucas Number = 7

6.85 410196624968454461376050309691435316092753941728858640634586811578138845 66658

- Phi^5

1.6180339887498948482045868343656381177203091798057628621^5

ans =   Lucas Number = 11

11.09 0169943749474241022934171828190588601545899028814310677243113526302314094428

- Phi^6

1.6180339887498948482045868343656381177203091798057628621^6

ans =   Lucas Number = 18

17.94 4271909999158785636694674925104941762473438446102897083588981642083702551057

• Phi^7

1.61803398874989484820458683436563811772030917980576286 21^7

ans =   Lucas Number = 29

29.034441853748633026659628846753295530364019337474917207760832095168386016645424

• Phi^8

1.61803398874989484820458683436563811772030917980576286 21^8

ans =   Lucas Number = 47

46.9787137637477918122963235216784004721264927759210201048444210768104697191 96382

• Phi^9

1.61803398874989484820458683436563811772030917980576286 21^9

ans =   Lucas Number = 76

76.01315561749642483895595236843169600249051211339593731260525317197 8855735841648

• Phi^10

1.61803398874989484820458683436563811772030917980576286 21^10

ans =   Lucas Number = 123

122.991869381244216651252275890110096474617004889316957417449674 24878932545503777

• Phi^11

1.61803398874989484820458683436563811772030917980576286 21^11

ans =   Lucas Number = 199

199.00502499874064149020822825854179247710751700271289473005492 7420768181190879

• Phi^12

1.61803398874989484820458683436563811772030917980576286 21^12

ans =   Lucas Number = 322

321.996894379984858141460504148651888951724521892029852147504601 6695575066459161

- Phi^13

1.6180339887498948482045868343656381177203091798057628621^13

ans =   Lucas Number = 521

521.00₁₉₁₉₃₇₈₇₂₅₄₉₉₆₃₁₆₆₈₇₃₂₄₀₇₁₉₃₆₈₁₄₂₈₈₃₂₀₃₈₈₉₄₇₄₂₇₄₆₈₇₇₅₅₉₅₂₉₀₉₀₃₂₅₆₈₇₈₃₆₇₉₄₀₂

- Phi^14

1.6180339887498948482045868343656381177203091798057628621^14

ans =   Lucas Number = 843

842.99₈₈₁₃₇₅₈₇₁₀₃₅₇₇₇₃₁₂₉₂₃₆₅₅₅₈₄₅₅₇₀₃₈₀₅₅₆₅₆₀₇₈₆₇₇₂₅₉₉₀₂₅₀₆₄₁₃₀₇₅₉₈₈₃₁₉₄₄₈₂₇₀₈₃₆

- Phi^15

1.6180339887498948482045868343656381177203091798057628621^15

ans =   Lucas Number = 1,364

1,364.00₀₇₃₃₁₃₇₄₃₅₈₅₇₄₀₄₇₉₇₉₆₈₉₆₃₀₃₉₂₅₁₈₀₉₃₈₈₅₉₉₆₈₁₅₁₅₃₄₅₉₀₂₆₂₃₆₅₉₈₅₀₂₀₈₈₈₂₃₁₉₄₉₉₅

- Phi^16

1.6180339887498948482045868343656381177203091798057628621^16

ans =   Lucas Number = 2,207

2,206.99₉₅₄₆₈₉₆₁₄₆₂₁₅₁₇₇₉₂₇₂₀₅₅₁₈₈₈₄₈₂₂₁₈₉₉₄₅₁₆₀₄₆₈₂₈₇₉₄₄₉₂₇₆₈₇₇₉₀₆₁₀₀₉₂₀₇₆₈₀₂₂₀₃₃

- Phi^17

1.6180339887498948482045868343656381177203091798057628621^17

ans =   Lucas Number = 3,571

3,571.00₀₂₈₀₀₃₃₅₈₂₀₇₂₅₈₂₇₂₅₁₇₄₄₈₁₉₂₄₀₇₃₉₉₉₃₃₃₇₆₀₁₄₉₈₀₃₂₉₀₈₃₀₃₁₁₄₅₀₄₆₀₃₀₀₉₅₉₁₂₁₆₉₅₃

- Phi^18

1.6180339887498948482045868343656381177203091798057628621^18

ans =   Lucas Number = 5,778

5,777.99₉₈₂₆₉₂₉₇₂₈₂₈₇₇₆₀₆₅₂₃₈₀₀₀₀₈₀₈₈₉₆₁₈₉₂₇₈₉₂₀₆₁₈₀₉₁₂₃₅₇₅₇₉₉₉₂₄₁₀₇₀₃₉₃₀₃₅₉₂₃₈₈₆₅

- **Phi^19**

1.618033988749894848204586834365638117720309179805762862 1^19

ans =   **Lucas Number = 9,349**

9,349.000106963310360343377554482732970188612680767894526588310691530693995045 5622

- **Phi^20**

1.618033988749894848204586834365638117720309179805762862 1^20

ans =   **Lucas Number = 15,127**

15,126.9999338930386481040299344835418663778916013859857623463099326010870309 69417

- **Phi^21**

1.618033988749894848204586834365638117720309179805762862 1^21

ans =   **Lucas Number = 24,476**

24,476.00004085634900844740748896627483656650428215388028893462062413178102601 4928

- **Phi^22**

1.618033988749894848204586834365638117720309179805762862 1^22

ans =   **Lucas Number = 39,603**

39,602.9999747493876565514374234498167029443958835398660512809305567328680569 84262

- **Phi^23**

1.618033988749894848204586834365638117720309179805762862 1^23

ans =   **Lucas Number = 64,079**

64,079.00001560573666499884491241609153951090016569374634021555118086464908299 9056

- **Phi^24**

1.618033988749894848204586834365638117720309179805762862 1^24

ans =   **Lucas Number = 103,682**

103,681.99999035512432155028233586590824245529604923361239149648173759751713 99831

• Phi^25

1.61803398874989484820458683436563811772030917980576286 21^25

ans =   Lucas Number = 167,761

167,761.00 0005960860986549127248281999781966196214927358731712032918462166222 98181

• Phi^26

1.61803398874989484820458683436563811772030917980576286 21^26

ans =   Lucas Number = 271,443

271,442.99 99963159853080994095841479080244214922641609711232085146560596833 6296434

• Phi^27

1.61803398874989484820458683436563811772030917980576286 21^27

ans =   Lucas Number = 439,204

439,204.00 00022768462946485368324299078063876884790883298549205475745218495 8594523

• Phi^28

1.61803398874989484820458683436563811772030917980576286 21^28

ans =   Lucas Number = 710,647

710,646.99 99985928316027479464165778158308091807432493009781290622305815329 4890808

• Phi^29

1.61803398874989484820458683436563811772030917980576286 21^29

ans =   Lucas Number = 1,149,851

1,149,851.00 0000869677897396483249007723637196869222337630833049609805103382534 8509

• Phi^30

1.61803398874989484820458683436563811772030917980576286 21^30

ans =   Lucas Number = 1,860,498

1,860,497.99 99994625095001444296655855394680060499655869318111786720356849154 837551

- ## Phi^31

1.6180339887498948482045868343656381177203091798057628621^31

ans =   Lucas Number = 3,010,349

3,010,349.00₀₀₀₀₃₃₂₁₈₇₃₉₇₅₄₀₉₁₂₉₁₄₅₉₃₂₆₃₁₀₅₂₀₂₉₁₉₁₈₇₉₂₄₅₆₂₆₄₄₂₂₈₂₈₁₈₄₀₇₈₈₂₉₈₀₁₈₅₉₉₇

- ## Phi^32

1.6180339887498948482045868343656381177203091798057628621^32

ans =   Lucas Number = 4,870,847

4,870,846.99₉₉₉₉₇₉₄₆₉₆₈₉₇₆₈₅₃₄₂₅₈₀₁₇₈₈₀₂₅₇₃₂₀₈₉₆₉₁₅₃₅₁₁₄₉₄₄₅₅₄₀₆₉₅₃₈₇₆₄₇₃₂₁₃₅₀₂₃₄₄₆

- ## Phi^33

1.6180339887498948482045868343656381177203091798057628621^33

ans =   Lucas Number = 7,881,196

7,881,196.00₀₀₀₀₁₂₆₈₈₄₂₉₅₂₂₆₂₅₅₄₉₄₇₇₂₀₆₅₆₇₈₄₁₁₈₈₈₃₄₁₄₃₆₀₅₇₀₉₉₆₃₅₂₃₅₇₁₇₂₆₁₅₁₁₅₂₀₉₂₇₈

- ## Phi^34

1.6180339887498948482045868343656381177203091798057628621^34

ans =   Lucas Number = 12,752,043

12,752,042.99₉₉₉₉₉₂₁₅₈₁₁₉₂₉₁₁₅₉₈₀₇₄₉₅₀₈₆₈₂₅₁₆₂₀₈₅₇₄₉₄₉₄₇₅₅₁₅₅₅₀₄₂₁₈₉₅₉₃₇₃₄₇₂₅₀₂₃₂₄₆

- ## Phi^35

1.6180339887498948482045868343656381177203091798057628621^35

ans =   Lucas Number = 20,633,239

20,633,239.00₀₀₀₀₀₄₈₄₆₅₄₈₈₁₃₇₈₅₃₅₆₉₇₂₂₉₃₃₉₃₀₀₃₂₇₄₅₈₃₆₃₈₃₆₀₈₆₅₄₆₇₇₄₂₅₃₁₀₉₉₆₂₃₆₅₄₄₁₃

- ## Phi^36

1.6180339887498948482045868343656381177203091798057628621^36

ans =   Lucas Number = 33,385,282

33,385,281.99₉₉₉₉₉₇₀₀₄₆₆₈₁₀₄₉₄₅₁₆₄₄₆₇₃₈₀₂₁₈₁₆₅₃₆₀₃₃₃₁₃₃₁₁₆₀₂₀₉₇₁₉₆₁₄₉₀₄₇₃₀₉₆₁₅₆₇₃₀₆

- **Phi^37**

1.6180339887498948482045868343656381177203091798057628621^37

ans =   **Lucas Number = 54,018,521**

54,018,521.0000000185121691873052143967361116863491677147688643970402157271981113 24

- **Phi^38**

1.6180339887498948482045868343656381177203091798057628621^38

ans =   **Lucas Number = 87,403,803**

87,403,802.9999999885588502367568590705382933399524990459290741166551204581596 78447

- **Phi^39**

1.6180339887498948482045868343656381177203091798057628621^39

ans =   **Lucas Number = 141,422,324**

141,422,324.00000000707101942406207346727440502630166676069793851369533618535 778947

- **Phi^40**

1.6180339887498948482045868343656381177203091798057628621^40

ans =   **Lucas Number = 228,826,127**

228,826,126.9999999562986966081893253781269836625416580662701263035045664351 746744

- **Phi^41**

1.6180339887498948482045868343656381177203091798057628621^41

ans =   **Lucas Number = 370,248,451**

370,248,451.000000027008890848810060050871033925558325673249511440457928288752 5614

- **Phi^42**

1.6180339887498948482045868343656381177203091798057628621^42

ans =   **Lucas Number = 599,074,578**

599,074,577.99999998330758745699938542899801758809998373951963774396249472392 72233

- **Phi^43**

1.6180339887498948482045868343656381177203091798057628621^43

ans =   **Lucas Number = 969,323,029**

969,323,029.00000000010316478305809445479869051513658309412769149184420423 0126797645

- **Phi^44**

1.6180339887498948482045868343656381177203091798057628621^44

ans =   **Lucas Number = 1,568,397,607**

1,568,397,606.999999999362406576280883090886706910175829315228878692838291 7736606955

- **Phi^45**

1.6180339887498948482045868343656381177203091798057628621^45

ans =   **Lucas Number = 2,537,720,636**

2,537,720,636.0000000003940544068618276388736120615416602565057936112803340 749286666

- **Phi^46**

1.6180339887498948482045868343656381177203091798057628621^46

ans =   **Lucas Number = 4,106,118,243**

4,106,118,242.999999999756460983142710729760318971717489571734672304118625 8485893535

- **Phi^47**

1.6180339887498948482045868343656381177203091798057628621^47

ans =   **Lucas Number = 6,643,838,879**

6,643,838,879.0000000001505153900045383686339310332591498282404659153989599 235180063

- **Phi^48**

1.6180339887498948482045868343656381177203091798057628621^48

ans =   **Lucas Number = 10,749,957,122**

10,749,957,121.99999999990697637314724909839425000497663939997513821951758 57

• Phi^49

1.6180339887498948482045868343656381177203091798057628621^49

ans =   Lucas Number = 17,393,796,001

17,393,796,001.00₀₀₀₀₀₀₀₀₀₅₇₄₉₁₇₆₃₁₅₁₇₈₇₄₆₇₀₂₈₁₈₁₀₃₈₂₃₅₇₈₉₂₂₈₂₁₅₆₀₄₁₃₄₉₁₆₅₄₅₆₉₅₆₂₅₃₀₇

17,393,796,001.000000000057491763151787467028181038235789228215604134916545695625307

• Phi^50

1.6180339887498948482045868343656381177203091798057628621^50

ans =   Lucas Number = 28,143,753,123

28,143,753,122.9999999999644681362990365654224310432124286281907423544343141467732586

(Art of Jain 1995, Angel Of Healing)

PATTERN OBSERVATION
IN THE LISTING FOR THE 50 POWERS OF PHI

Did you notice any patterns in the above data?

Here are three observations:

1 - There is a pattern in the Powers of Phi when reduced to whole numbers and called the Lucas Numbers. They go:

Odd, Odd, Even

Odd, Odd, Even

Odd, Odd, Even

Odd, Odd, Even

Odd, Odd, Even

2 - There is an increasing repetition of "0"s and "9"s after the decimal point, alternating with lots of zeroes or lots of nines

eg: phi^41

ans = 370,248,451.00000000₂₇₀₀₈₈₉₀₈₄₈₈₁₀₀₆₀₀₅₀₈₇₁₀₃₃₉₂₅₅₅₈₃₂₅₆₇₃₂₄₉₅₁₁₄₄₀₄₅₇₉₂₈₂₈₈₇

ans = 370,248,451.00000000 27008890848810060050871033925558325673249511440457928287

eg: phi^42

ans = 599,074,577.99999999 83307587456999385428998017588099983739519637743962494239

It is actually quite a remarkable pattern, this anomaly has not been seen anywhere else, not that I know of.

3 - The 24th Power of Phi is the end of the cycle, because the next 24 Powers repeat the same digitally compressed pattern. We can call this the 1st Set of 24. Therefore the beginning of 2nd Set of 24 is the number: ϕ^{25} which is **167,761 a Palindromic Number (reading the same forwards as backwards).**

Now that we have worked out all of the Powers Of Phi (POP) to 50 Powers and have lots of big answers with long trailing decimal points, like Phi^50 = just over 28 trillion, we need to put the same information into a neat table, just to bring closure to this part. From this table we can inspect whether or not there is indeed a repeating 24 pattern, that's why I went to 50 powers of phi since 24x2=48 and this is enough info to confirm that 2 cycles or Sets of 24 are clearly repetitive.

LEGEND: for Fig 1 following.

No. = Number

NI = Nearest Integer

LN = Lucas Number Series 1, 3, 4, 7, 11, 18, 29, 47

DP = Decimal Places

DS = Digital Sum eg: 199 = 1+9+9 = 19 = 1+9 =10 =1+0 = 1

or just "Cast Out The Nines" from 199 means delete the 2 nines and it leaves the 1.

ON = Odd Number

EN = Even Number

Phi^n = *Phi to the power of "n" where "n" is the natural counting numbers like 1, 2, 3, 4, etc*

Creative spiral calligraphy of the word "Infinity".

(source unknown, taken from a book on chaos theory or fractal geometry)

Just a short note or anomaly regarding the next table of numbers,
Fig 1, pertaining to the first line of data:

No. of Phi Power Phi^n	Answer for Phi^n based on 77 dp	Nearest Integer	Lucas Number	Odd or Even	Digital Sum
1	1.618033988749...	1	1	Odd	1

The Phi Ratio is 1.618... but for all purposes to make it similar to the Lucas Number Series, I am writing in the number "1" as the Nearest Integer, not "2" as it is meant to be phi^1 = 1.618033988... is actually closer to the even number "2" than it is to 1.

This is the only anomaly in the chart.

I want you to compare the far right column on both following pages where the Digital Sums appear, and you will see that they are both identical, in that the 24 repeating Pattern is indeed recursive and self-similar. This could only happen by making the change above, writing down a 1 instead of a 2.

Perhaps to get the "1" as the starting point of the Lucas Number series, we know that Phi or any number to the power of zero, equals "1".

That is: phi^0 = 1.

Thus the first line should really look like this:

0	1		1	1	Odd	1

It implies that phi^1 is not being determined, that is, it is skipped. The Lucas Sequence, as you will see in the following table has a distinct trinity progression of **"Odd, Odd then Even"**, another reason why the first number should be an odd number "1" and not an even number "2".

---

2 PAGE SUMMARY CHART SHOWING ALL DATA UP TO THE 50TH POWER OF PHI EXPRESSED AS "PHI^50"

No. of Phi Power Phi^n	Answer for Phi^n based on 77 dp	Nearest Integer	Lucas Number	Odd or Even	Digital Sum
0 or 1	1 or 1.61803398...	1	1	Odd	1
2	2.618033988749...	3	3	Odd	3
3	4.236067977499...	4	4	Even	4
4	6.854101966249...	7	7	Odd	7
5	11.09016994374...	11	11	Odd	2
6	17.94427190999...	18	18	Even	9
7	29.03444185374...	29	29	Odd	2
8	46.97871376374...	47	47	Odd	2
9	76.01315561749...	76	76	Even	4
10	122.9918693812...	123	123	Odd	6
11	199.0050249987...	199	199	Odd	1
12	321.9968943799...	322	322	Even	7
13	521.0019193787...	521	521	Odd	8
14	842.9988137587...	843	843	Odd	6
15	1,364.00073313...	1,364	1,364	Even	5
16	2,206.99954689...	2,207	2,207	Odd	2
17	3,571.000280033...	3,571	3,571	Odd	7
18	5,777.999826929...	5,778	5,778	Even	9
19	9,349.000106963...	9,349	9,349	Odd	7
20	15,126.99993389...	15,127	15,127	Odd	7
21	24,476.00004085...	24,476	24,476	Even	5
22	39,602.99997474...	39,603	39,603	Odd	3
23	64,079.00001560...	64,079	64,079	Odd	8
24	103,681.9999903...	103,682	103,682	Even	2

No. of Phi Power Phi^n	Answer for Phi^n based on 77 dp	Nearest Integer	Lucas Number	Odd or Even	Digital Sum
25	167,761.000005960...	167,761	167,761	Odd	1
26	271,442.999996315...	271,443	271,443	Odd	3
27	439,204.000002276...	439,204	439,204	Even	4
28	710,646.999998592...	710,647	710,647	Odd	7
29	1,149,851.0000008...	1,149,851	1,149,851	Odd	2
30	1,860,497.9999994...	1,860,498	1,860,498	Even	9
31	3,010,349.0000003...	3,010,349	3,010,349	Odd	2
32	4,870,846.9999997...	4,870,847	4,870,847	Odd	2
33	7,881,196.0000001...	7,881,196	7,881,196	Even	4
34	12,752,042.999999...	12,752,043	12,752,043	Odd	6
35	20,633,239.000000...	20,633,239	20,633,239	Odd	1
36	33,385,281.999999...	33,385,282	33,385,282	Even	7
37	54,018,521.000000...	54,018,521	54,018,521	Odd	8
38	87,403,802.999999...	87,403,803	87,403,803	Odd	6
39	141,422,324.00000...	141,422,324	141,422,324	Even	5
40	228,826,126.99999...	228,826,127	228,826,127	Odd	2
41	370,248,451.00000...	370,248,451	370,248,451	Odd	7
42	599,074,577.99999...	599,074,578	599,074,578	Even	9
43	969,323,029.00000...	969,323,029	969,323,029	Odd	7
44	1,568,397,606.9999...	1,568,397,607	1,568,397,607	Odd	7
45	2,537,720,636.0000...	2,537,720,636	2,537,720,636	Even	5
46	4,106,118,242.9999...	4,106,118,243	4,106,118,243	Odd	3
47	6,643,838,879.0000...	6,643,838,879	6,643,838,879	Odd	8
48	10,749,957,121.999...	10,749,957,122	10,749,957,122	Even	2
49	17,393,796,001.000...	17,393,796,001	17,393,796,001	Odd	1
50	28,143,753,122.999...	28,143,753,123	28,143,753,123	Odd	3

Fig 1

or Table 1

Tabulating The Powers of Phi up to the 50th Power,

Tabulating The Powers of Phi up to the 50th Power,

using 77 Decimal Places

to examine if there exists REPEATABILITY in the digitally reduced powers shown
in the far right hand column.

OBSERVATIONS: THE "24 REPEATING LUCAS SEQUENCE", AND THE "ODD, ODD, EVEN" PATTERN

There appears to be a distinct recursion

of the digitally compressed Powers Of Phi.

Here again is the Repeating 24 Pattern of the Powers of Phi:

It is identical to what Mathematician's know as

The Lucas Numbers

1	3	4	7	2	9	2	2	4	6	1	7	8	6	5	2	7	9	7	7	5	3	8	2

Fig 2

Powers Of Phi Code 108:

Is the Lucas Sequence:

an Infinitely Repeating 24 Pattern based on the

Digital Compression of the Powers Of Phi into Single Digits.

This one is termed Multi-Dimensional, aka PHI CODE 2.

ORIGIN OF THE MEDICAL SYMBOL: CADUCEUS

Here are some graphics of the well-known Caduceus symbol that is the representation of Phi Code 2.

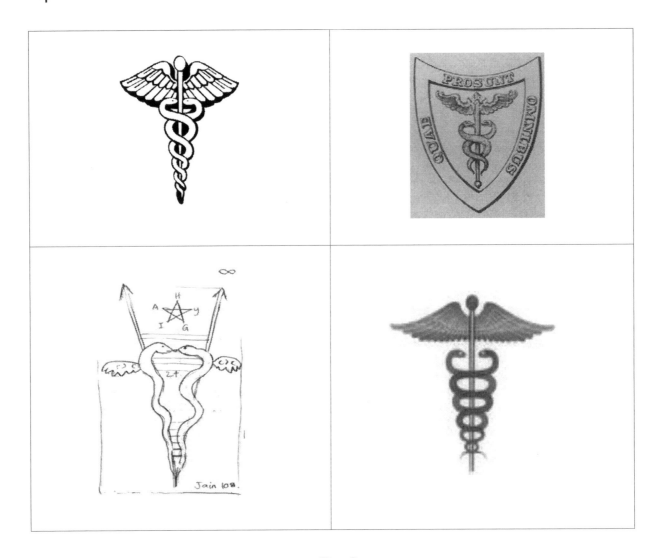

Fig 3
Famous Medical Symbol, the Caduceus,
when seen as a ladder of increasing rungs, has it's stairway lengths
going up to Heaven (Infinity) equal to the distances of the Powers of Phi.

Big Pharma has claimed this most powerful symbol, and we need to reclaim and purify it, now. (Also to be aware of Big Ag, Big Oil, Big Military etc).
The two entwining winged snakes can also represent the Ida and Pingala that surround the central Shushumna column akin to the spinal column, or the two voluntary and involuntary nervous network systems.
On another level, these counter-rotating helices are our DNA.

CONCLUSION:

So, in this analysis of all the above material,

I have concluded that there exists a distinct hidden sequence of 108

based on the Powers Of Phi,

which are akin to or linked to

the famous Lucas Numbers adored by stock marketeers.

I am convinced from this material

and based on my knowledge of the Powers of Phi

that this is lost Ancient Knowledge that was once known as

the "Jacob's Multi-Dimensional Ladder"

or what we sing as The Stairway To Heaven

This ancient Knowledge is hidden in the Medical Symbol

of the 2 DNA-like serpents winding around the winged Staff,

it's overall geometry is a forever non-ending "V" shape,

each rung of the ladder is yet another Power of Phi,

an excellent symbol for Infinity.

And imbued in this nest of ratios is the 108ness.

The current tragedy is that this symbol that carries this Knowledge

has been recently utilized by the Big Pharma companies

claiming it as their winged Caduceus Symbol

used by the medical profession, by cursing it

to eugenically poison the populations

with their chemo-therapies and secretly creating and funding wars.

We can reclaim this "V" knowledge by holding strong our Pure Intentions,

and dedicating these Anointed Frequencies for Higher Purposes.

These sequences can also be creatively applied to

musical scales and colour frequencies etc

to assist in the healing of the body, mind and spirit.

Our job is merely to reclaim this symbol.

Jain 108

On DIVISION Of NEIGHBOURING Or CONSECUTIVE LUCAS NUMBERS

Let us discover what is the proportion from one lucas number to the succeeding lucas number,

Just like with the Fibonacci sequence where each number is in the 1.618... proportion.

1 = 3 ÷ 1 = 3

3 = 4 ÷ 3 = 1.3333...

4 = 7 ÷ 4 = 1.75

7 = 11 ÷ 7 = 1.428571...

11 = 18 ÷ 11 = 1.63636363...

18 = 29 ÷ 18 = 1.6111111111...

and try some larger Lucas or Powers Of Phi numbers on the chart:

17,393,796,001 = 28,143,753,123 ÷ 17,393,796,001

$\qquad\qquad$ = 1.618033988...

etc

Notice that the successive divisions will naturally converge to 1.618033...

Actually, any two numbers that give a Fibonacci type of progression will always converge to 1.618033... this is just another remarkable property of the Phi ratio.

I believe that what is so special about Phi Code 1 (PC1,1,2) is that it is the first primal pattern and it is the quickest sequence that gets direct to converging on Phi or 1.618033... This makes PC1 as highly efficient energy.

eg: you can start with any two random numbers like 6 & 9 and add them in the style of the Fibonacci Sequence (ie: 6+9=15, and 9+15=24) etc and when you divide one number by it's predecessor you always come back to this mysterious ratio 1:1.618033... In fact, it is not even a number, it is a relationship of cascading frequencies.

Really this is a remarkable statement, because in effect it is saying that everything in the Universe converges back to Phi, regardless whether it is an additive (PC1) or a multiplicative (PC2) sequence.

ALL FALSE DATA UP TO THE 50TH POWER OF PHI USING PHI TO 9 DECIMAL PLACES
(THE VERSION THAT BROKE DOWN AFTER THE 35th DP)

This following material or chapter was the original mathematics that raised Phi to the 50th Power, but no symmetry was found, as it turned out that using Phi to only 9 decimal places as is standard on the electronic calculator, failed to show any repeatability.

Six months goes by, and I have the inspiration to do it all again, this time using CCalc, a free internet download, that gave me up to 80 dp accuracy. This was enough to x-ray the new data, self-correct itself and find repeatability or recursiveness.

(I remember about 20 years ago, a wise old Masonic teacher came up to me and said something very cryptic. Regarding "Pattern Hunting", he said, that I would "not get it" until I examined decimalized numbers greater than 33 decimal places. This has turned out to be very true.

Rather than discarding this following section, since there are many inaccuracies which appear around the Phi^36 mark, I choose to include it in this book for mere use as a trial reference towards the correct discovery. If you discard this article, all you need to know is that "How to crack the code was dependent upon having a calculator utilizing up to 80 decimal places". This is therefore really a tribute to Technology. This 24 Repeating Recursive Pattern in the Powers of Phi could not have been realized by hand calculation nor with a simple pocket calculator with 9 decimal points!

(USING CCALC TRUE UP TO 9 DECIMAL PLACES DP)

Phi = 1.618033988...

Allowing Phi to the Power of Zero = 1

> Phi^0 = 1   Lucas Number = 1

[Omit this:

Let Phi=1.618033988...

Phi^1 = 1. 1.618033988   Lucas Number = 2]

> Phi^2

ans = 2.618033986...   Lucas Number = 3

> Phi^3

ans = 4.236067971...   Lucas Number = 4

> Phi^4

ans = 6.854101953 ...   Lucas Number = 7

> Phi^5

ans = 11.090169918...   Lucas Number = 11

> Phi^6

ans = 17.944271860...   Lucas Number = 18

> Phi^7

ans = 29.034441759...   Lucas Number = 29

> Phi^8

ans = 46.978713589...   Lucas Number = 47

> Phi^9

ans = 76.013155300...

Lucas Number = 76

> Phi^10

ans = 122.991868811...

Lucas Number = 123

> Phi^11

ans = 199.005023984...

Lucas Number = 199

> Phi^12

ans = 321.996892589...

Lucas Number = 322

> Phi^13

ans = 521.001916239...

Lucas Number = 521

> Phi^14

ans = 842.998808288...

Lucas Number = 843

> Phi^15

ans = 1,364.000723655...

Lucas Number = 1,364

> Phi^16

ans = 2,206.999530530...

Lucas Number = 2,207

> Phi^17

ans = 3,571.000251898...

Lucas Number = 3,571

> Phi^18

ans = 5,777.999778727...

Lucas Number = 5,778

> Phi^19

ans = 9,349.000024638...

Lucas Number = 9,349

> Phi^20

ans = 15,126.999793677...

Lucas Number = 15,127

> Phi^21

ans = 24,475.999802639...

Lucas Number = 24,476

> Phi^22

ans = 39,602.999570952...

Lucas Number = 39,603

> Phi^23

ans = 64,078.999332549...

Lucas Number = 64,079

> Phi^24

ans = 103,681.998837094...

Lucas Number = 103,682

> Phi^25

ans = 167,760.998062195...

Lucas Number = 167,761

> Phi^26

ans = 271,442.996725435...

Lucas Number = 271,443

> Phi^27

ans = 439,203.994506326...

Lucas Number = 439,204

> Phi^28

ans = 710,646.990776602...

Lucas Number = 710,647

> Phi^29

ans = 1,149,850.984546464...   Lucas Number = 1,149,851

> Phi^30

ans = 1,860,497.974131442...   Lucas Number = 1,860,498

> Phi^31

ans = 3,010,348.956749818...   Lucas Number = 3,010,349

 > Phi^32

ans = 4,870,846.927761548...   ucas Number = 4,870,847

> Phi^33

ans = 7,881,195.879463566...   Lucas Number = 7,881,196

> Phi^34

ans = 12,752,042.799057601...   Lucas Number = 12,752,043

> Phi^35

ans = 20,633,238.665305853...   Lucas Number = 20,633,239

> Phi^36

ans = 33,385,281.442980627...

False Lucas Number = 33,385,281

*** FIRST ERROR THAT APPEARS ***

SINCE The CORRECT ANSWER Or The 36TH LUCAS NUMBER Is 33,385,282

as shown in Fig 1: the table with the 77 dp. This suggests that all data after this point is fallacious or in error:

> Phi^37

ans = 54,018,520.073688340...

False Lucas Number = 54,018,520

Error, should be 54,018,521

> Phi^38

ans = 87,403,801.460687998...

False Lucas Number = 87,403,801

Error, should be 87,403,803

> Phi^39

ans = 141,422,321.443797227...

False Lucas Number = 141,422,321

Error, should be 141,422,324

> Phi^40

ans = 228,826,122.757925146...

False Lucas Number = 228,826,123

Error, should be 228,826,127

> Phi^41

ans = 370,248,443.964583183...

False Lucas Number = 370,248,444

Error, should be 370,248,451

> Phi^42

ans = 599,074,566.338809058...

False Lucas Number = 599,074,566

Error, should be 599,074,578

> Phi^43

ans = 969,323,009.682553780...

False Lucas Number = 969,323,010

Error, should be 969,323,029

> Phi^44

ans = 1,568,397,575.016825107...

False Lucas Number = 1,568,397,575

Error, should be 1,568,397,607

> Phi^45

ans = 2,537,720,583.074002695...

False Lucas Number = 2,537,720,583

Error, should be 2,537,720,636

> Phi^46

ans = 4,106,118,155.460913881...

False Lucas Number = 4,106,118,155

Error, should be 4,106,118,243

> Phi^47

ans = 6,643,838,734.279626465...

False Lucas Number = 6,643,838,734

Error, should be 6,643,838,879

> Phi^48

ans = 10,749,956,882.855336316...

False Lucas Number = 10,749,956,883

Error, should be 10,749,957,122

> Phi^49

ans = 17,393,795,605.994468647...

False Lucas Number = 17,393,795,606

Error, should be 17,393,796,001

> Phi^50

ans = 28,143,752,470.824106811...

False Lucas Number = 28,143,752,471

Error, should be 28,143,753,123

Fig 4 or Table 2

This body of incorrect data expresses the Powers of Phi
based insufficiently on 9 Decimal Places.
(You need to refer to Table 1 for the correct data
based on 77 Decimal Places).

Have a look at the discrepancy between the Powers of Phi up to the 50th Power shown here, using Phi to only 9 dp.

(phi^50 = 28,143,752,471)

and compare it to using Phi to a precise 77 dp

(Phi^50 = 28,143,753,123)

The difference or grand error is a staggering 652, which although appeared precise using 9dp, the minute errors accumulated and went pear shaped around Phi to the 36th power.

Also, in the last table using 9 dp, none of the decimals, after the decimal point, showed any of the beauty apparent in the previous table with 77 dp where the numbers after the decimal point repeated either with .00000000 or .9999999 consistently.

This was a valuable lesson in the art of extreme accuracy.

HYGIA, HEALTH AND
SACRED GEOMETRY CONNECTIONS

I would like to conclude by stating again, my tribute to technology, just like how Ulam's Rose of Prime Numbers could not have been discovered until the advent of computers, similarly, this 24 infinitely recursive pattern in the Powers of Phi Caduceus could not have been realized by hand calculation. It implies, that if Big Pharma who monopolize this symbol, have ancient and sophisticated knowledge that only an intelligent race could have possessed this.

Part of the dissemination of these Phi Codes of 108, is to pass this knowledge to the next generation and have these students reclaim the symbol of ancient healing, that it be claimed by the organic and living food revolution for the upliftment of all human beings who share this planet and seek good physical health and astral hygiene.

The best that we can do until this change happens, is for you to take personal responsibility for your health, by seeking pure uncontaminated waters to drink, and increase your quota of living foods that you ingest. But above all, have fun.

The ancient symbol for the lost Pythagorean order, was the Blue Pentacle or 5 pointed star. On each of the 5 vertices, there was a Greek letter of the alphabet, that when read as a word, spelt HYGIA the goddess of Healing and the origin of our word "Hygiene". This was the case two and a half thousand years ago, that to live in the Pythagorean community, you had to do lots of fasting and hygiene maintenance, that before you could receive the highest mathematical codes, you had to be cleansed and ready to receive it so that you could apply it to higher principle and not for selfish gain.

The Pythagoreans used The Pentagram or the "triple triangle" as a symbol and badge of the Society of Pythagoras. By this sign they recognised a fellow member. This pentagram Star was also regarded as a symbol of HEALTH: the five angles being the letters "ΥΓΙΘΑ" which G the Greek word 4 Health denoted by please draw this star upon your Door. © Jain. 2.7.1996.

Fig 5

Pentacle with Pythagorean encryption of 5 Greek Letters
spelling H-Y-G-I-A or Hygiea:
The Goddess of Health and Healing.
This establishes a direct line with Sacred Geometry and Nutrition.

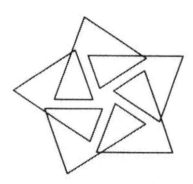

Fig 5a

SpiralLateral, Pentacle formed from 72 degree turns!

This Pentacle is a very Psycho-Active diagram as it is stored in the memory of the Mass Consciousness, mainly because the Pent is the basic shape of all living Proteins in the Human Cells. This is one reason why it was demonized, the inverted pentacle being the symbol of the Christian Devil.

Fig 5b

Frustum – sliced Pentagonal Pyramid Fold-Up Diagram

EXPRESSION OF THE POWERS OF PHI
IN TERMS OF THE FIBONACCI NUMBERS

Have a look at this most interesting pattern,

(first written onto the web by David Thomson in Jul 2006)

Phi^1 = Phi

Phi^2 = Phi(0+1Phi)

Phi^3 = Phi(1+1Phi)

Phi^4 = Phi(1+2Phi)

Phi^5 = Phi(2+3Phi)

Phi^6 = Phi(3+5Phi)

Phi^7 = Phi(5+8Phi)

Phi^8 = Phi(8+13Phi)

Phi^9 = Phi(13+21Phi)

Phi^{10} = Phi(21+34Phi)

Phi^{11} = Phi(34+55Phi)

Phi^{12} = Phi(55+89Phi)

Fig 6

Expression of the Powers of Phi in terms of the Fibonacci Numbers!

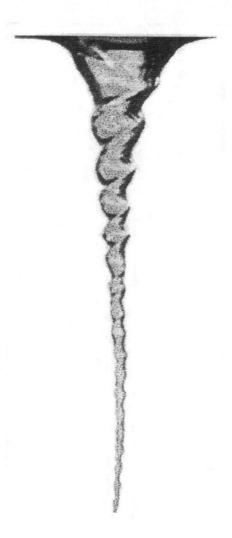

Fig 7
Twisting Water Tornado as the Powers of Phi.

Really, what is the translation, in physical terms,

of this mathematical vorticity?

It's simple, it's about "**getting sucked in**"

or movement towards the center, towards the heart.

The secret of water, is not only that it means **LIQUID LIGHT**

(In Hebrew, the word for water is a compound word, that is,

being made up of two parts or words:

first part is "**MEM**" = **Water**,

and second part is "**ORI**" = **Light**,

thus water = memory, liquid light....

WATER = MATER

And, here is another beautiful calligraphic secret about Water,
(thanks to my friend and teacher Callum Coats, of the Sunshine Coast, and
translator of the Viktor Schauberger material)

who illustrated that "WATER" is "MATER"

that there is no other word in the English language, that when the first letter
"W" of the word is flipped over 180 degrees, that it forms another coherent or
recognizable word starting with "M".

Fig 8
WATER~MATER

MATER is the Mother

MATER is the Matter or Physical Substance

WATER is element of divine creation, it is our Life.

That is why this book is a tribute to the current and next generation of children
to fight the star war battle of preserving the purity of all our flowing and non-
flowing creeks and river streams, as they are no different that the blood that
runs through our veins, just like the Amazon Forest is the lungs of Mother Earth,
the water is the anatomical lymph system.

Water is Mater:
Water is our Mother.

FAQ

QUESTION 1: Why is that you state that this Phi Code is to be revealed as INITIATE KNOWLEDGE ?

ANSWER: The reason for the protectiveness around the
dissemination of this Phi Code 2 is that it has never been printed
before in such detail, nor released to the world as such,
thus it is like guarded Celestial Knowledge,
and as a Guardian of this Code,
as a Farmer of Magic Square Matrices
my job is to ensure that it goes to those who are Engrailed,
who will hold this code
as if they would care for a loved crystal,
and in a similar fashion, program it with Thoughts of Peace and
Love for the Fibonaccization of the Planet,
to bring global unity above all other costs and factors.
Your Heart is Pure, your Intent is Pure,
thus it has come to You.
How you work with this Phi Code 2
is your personal challenge, whether you attribute the numbers
to specific frequencies or musical notes,
or build it as a children's playground
or make it into a 108 beaded rosary
or use it in your building constructions
or colour code as tiles on your floor;
this code is strengthened by your buddha field, your love and
intent. One condition for receiving this
is that you do not pass it on to others ad lib, as I would prefer that
any student wanting this Higher Code needs to jump through some
hoops or loops, referring to them
to attend the 12 day Jain Mathemagics Seminars
so they grok the pure principles of
Translating Numbers Into Art
The Universal Language of Shape and Pattern
The Joy and innate Beauty of Numbers
The inter-connectedness of all life
to SEE GOD IN ALL PEOPLE AND ALL THINGS.

QUESTION 2:
What is this relationship between Sacred Geometry and the "Holy Grail"?

ANSWER:
Some authors have translated the word "Grail" to mean "Pattern" or a Consecrated Pattern. Our search for this Grail or Holy Pattern is the quest for our deeper selves, that which is in our DNA, in our cells, that which we have carried within us all this time, this endless time. The same pattern in the human canon is the same mathematics that determines the arc in architecture. If you wanted a definition of what Sacred Geometry is, then it must include this reference to a divine universal Language of Shape and Pattern that which is found in the atom, in the human and in the galaxy, that is, on all levels, in all dimensions; for we do not really know if there are no dimensions or multi-dimension, all I know is that we will not find it in books or from other teachers, it is more a Journey into your own Creation story, our own Centre that is nowhere, yet everywhere and strangely has no centre since each point in space is a veritable centre. Ultimately, it is your Intent, that is the metaphysical Grail, for every word you speak and every thought that preceded that word, is a vibration or **"organized blueprint"** that has a pattern, and has the power to be made manifest, for what you focus on, is what you become. See God in All. There is no "Other". The Grid or **Net of Indra** that surrounds the planet is no different than the grid around the etheric human bio-temple.

Jain 108
12-12-2008 Mullumbimby

~ CHAPTER 4 ~

THE 3 – 6 – 9 SEQUENCE, THE ENNEAGRAM AND OTHER FACTS

This chapter includes:

- The Appearance of 3-6-9 in the 3 Phi Codes
- The Fraction 1/7 Plotted on the 9 Point Circle
- The Traditional Form of the Enneagram
- Creation of the Enneagram
- The Anointed Number 1089
- Worksheets
- Rings Of 24
- Derivation of the 144 Harmonic of Light

- Isolating the Hidden 3-6-9 Pattern

- Solutions + Solfeggio Scale Triplets

THE APPEARANCE OF 3 – 6 – 9 IN THE 3 PHI CODES

Notice that either of the 3 Numbers: 3, 6, 9 appear as every 4th letter in the 3 Phi Codes. I have highlighted every 4th number in a larger font:

— PHI CODE 1 (1,1,2)

1, 1, 2, **3**, 5, 8, 4, **3**, 7, 1, 8, **9**, 8, 8, 7, **6**, 4, 1, 5, **6**, 2, 8, 1, **9**

— PHI CODE 2 (1,3,4)

1, **3**, 4, 7, 2, **9**, 2, 2, 4, **6**, 1, 7, 8, **6**, 5, 2, 7, **9**, 7, 7, 5, **3**, 8, 2

— PHI CODE 3 (1,4,5)

1, 4, 5, **9**, 5, 5, 1, **6**, 7, 4, 2, **6**, 8, 5, 4, **9**, 4, 4, 8, **3**, 2, 5, 7, **3**

It appears that the main primal sequence of 6 numbers, when viewed in a circle and not a line, for all 3 Phi Codes, goes in this order:

$$3 - 3 - 9 - 6 - 6 - 9$$

(nb: for more comprehensive info on Phi Code 3, see the next volume called:
titled: THE BOOK OF PHI, volume 6:
sub-titled: THE 3 PHI CODES).

THE FRACTION 1/7 PLOTTED ON THE 9 POINT CIRCLE AS HALF OF THE ENNEAGRAM

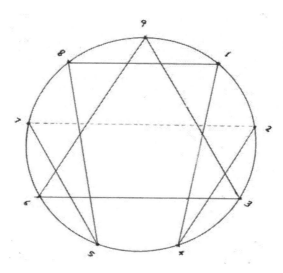

Fig 1

A typical image of the ancient 9 Pointed Star Enneagram

The famous Enneagram, or 9-pointed star that maps archetypes of consciousness, is commonly associated as coming from a Sufi tradition, but many other cultures have tapped into this wheel of personalities.
I
Traditionally, the Enneagram is believed to be a compound or superimposition of two important sequences based on 3 and 7.

The 3 is obvious, it is the 3-6-9 being the missing numbers in the decimal of 1/7.

The 7 is sacred as it does not divide the circle, since the 360 degrees divided by 7 is not a whole number, so many people think that the decimalization of 7 is occult. When you divide 1 by 7, that is, 1 ÷ 7, which is what we call the reciprocal of 7, you get a non-ending or infinitely repeating decimal answer called .142857142857142857 which can be looked at as:

.**142857** 142857 142857 which has a periodicity of 6. When you take these 6 digits of "1-4-2-8-5-7 and rewrite as triplets, you get:

```
1   4   2  +
8   5   7
─────────────
9   9   9
```

Notice that the triplets are seen as pairs that add up to 9, which gives us our first clue, to plug this data of 142857 into the infinitely recycling 9 Point Circle.

Also, **142857 x 7 = 999999**. And of course 1 divided by 3 yields an infinite sequence of threes. The triangle joining points 3, 6 and 9 links all the numbers on the circle divisible by 3.

Dividing one by three yields the decimals .3333, .6666, .9999 - the points joined by the triangle in the figure.

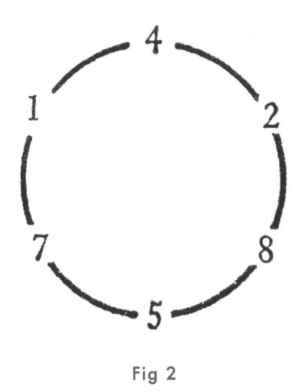

Fig 2

Decimalized Fraction 1/7 put into a Circle...

This circular diagram is important to help the student know, without use of the electronic calculator, the next fraction say 2/7 (and al the others like 6/7). To know the answer, you look at the above wheel, and find the next number above 1, which is "2" and reading clockwise, you see that the sequence of 6 numbers is 2-8-5-7-1-4 hinting that the decimal form answer for 2/7 is .285714 repeater...

INTRODUCTION and NOTES
ABOUT the ENNEAGRAM

The **Enneagram** is a circle divided by nine points equally spaced with the 3rd 6th and 9th parts being the endpoints of a triangle (Law of Three). The other points, 1st, 2nd, 4th, 5th, 7th, and 8th create a 6 pointed figure that intersect the large equilateral triangle at 12 points on the triangle and have 6 points on the circle. A curious thing is the **Menorah** of Jewish lore, it too, has nine points and if one were to look down from above it and the branches were moved you could see the points of the enneagram.

Many inspired people have formed whole cults and institutes around this 9-ness, in the same sense that the Zodiac has 12 signs and represent the **Labours of Hercules**, aspects of his ego that needed to be slain or conquered, so too is the Enneagram, but based on 9-ness.

Here is a typical school of the Enneagram that divides human nature into 9 categories (but dont get caught in the attributed meanings as various schools have various attributes, so it is not really universal):

Fig 3

A typical image of the ancient 9 Pointed Star Enneagram,

shown here as an archetypal map of consciousness or human personalities.

JAIN MATHEMAGICS WORKSHEET

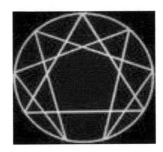

Here is a small exercise for you to get a feeling for the traditional Enneagram.

The following 2 diagrams of Fig 4 and Fig 5 are the 9 Point Circle, upon which you are going to draw the two above expressions of the Triad and the Reciprocal of 7.

Fig 4 and Fig 5 are the 2 blank worksheets, and Fig 5a is the solution to them.

Choose two colours. In one colour, connect the 3 to 6 to 9 to get the Equilateral Triangle or Triad shape.

Then superimpose upon this triangle, with another colour, the connection of the 6 repeating numbers of the reciprocal of 7: 1-4-2-8-5-7. This means that you are going to draw a long continuous line from 1 to 4 to 2 to 8 to 5 to 7, and back to the beginning again, a joining of the dots, to look for order amidst the chaos, to translate Number into Art, to make the invisible visible.

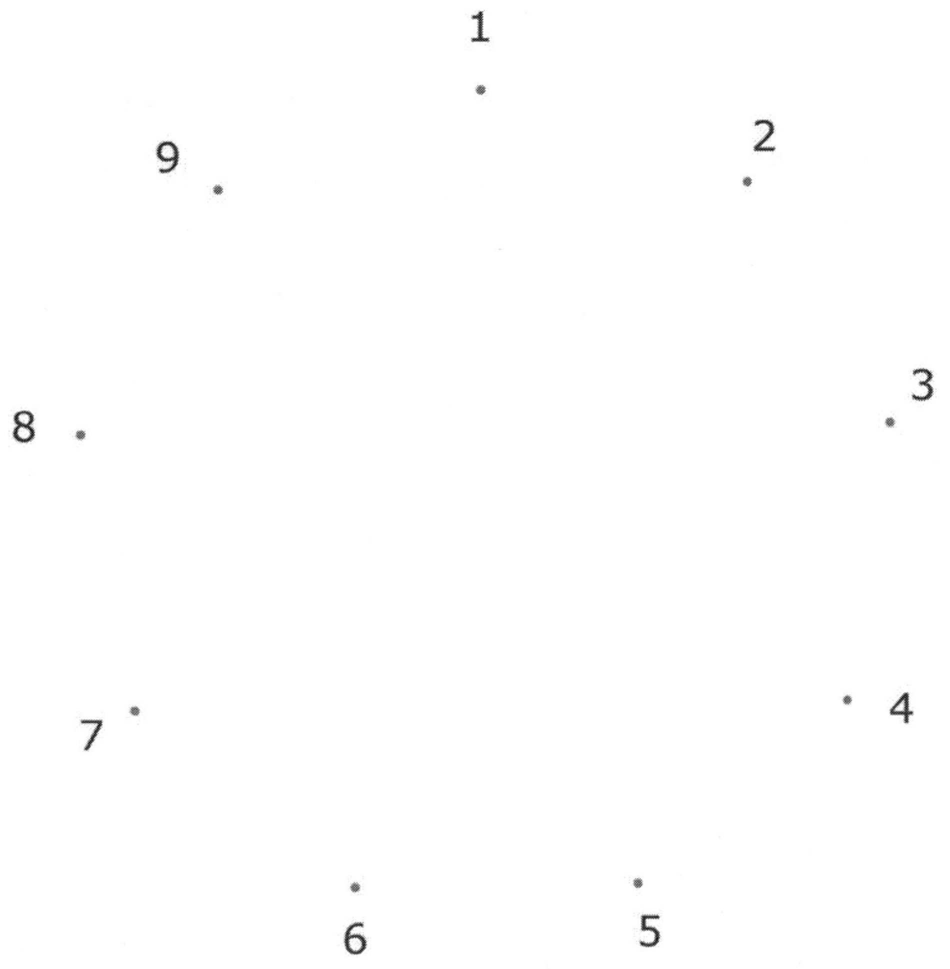

1

9

2

8

3

7

4

6   5

The Circle Of 9 Dots, Numbered from 1 to 9

Fig 4

The 9 Point Circle upon which you will draw the Enneagram,
using two colours to superimpose the Triad (3-6-9) and the Reciprocal of 7

3-6-9 PATTERN

$.\overline{142857}$
FRACTION 1/7

+

EQUALS

CREATION of ENNEAGRAM

Fig 5
A typical Jain Mathemagics Worksheet:
The 9 Point Circle upon which you will draw the Enneagram

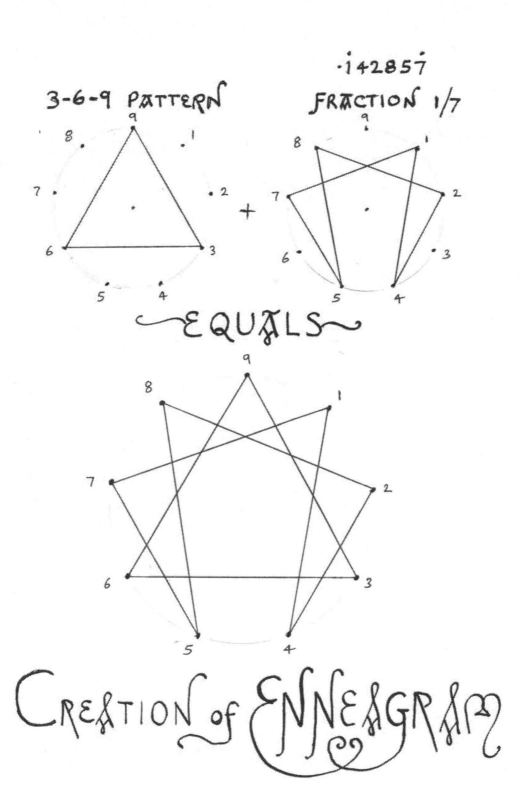

3-6-9 PATTERN

.i42857
FRACTION 1/7

+

~EQUALS~

CREATION of ENNEAGRAM

Fig 5a
A typical Jain Mathemagics Worksheet, Solution:
The 9 Point Circle Generating the Enneagram.
The top two patterns combine to form the traditional Enneagram.

The ANOINTED NUMBER 1089

(This mathematical page is given only to highlight the importance of the triad or sanctity of 3ness).

In previous chapters, I had shown the infinitely repeating 24 Pattern of the Powers of Phi, had a debatable sum of 108 or 117 (108+9).

1	3	4	7	2	9	2	2	4	6	1	7
8	6	5	2	7	9	7	7	5	3	8	2

Of interest, is that the pattern has a double nine bond, so it is really expressed as:

108 - 9 - 108 – 9 - 108 – 9 - 108 - 9 - 108 – 9 - 108 – 9 etc

which can be fancifully viewed as **1089**.
What number, when squared, or multiplied by itself gives this number 1089?
Or, the same thing is to ask, what is the square root of 1,089?

The answer is **33**. Number 33, is another sacred number held in high regard by many cultures and secret organizations. eg: the 33rd degree of Masonic initiation.

$$3^2 = 9$$
$$33^2 = 1089$$
$$333^2 = 110889$$
$$3333^2 = 11108889$$
$$33333^2 = 1111088889$$
$$333333^2 = 111110888889$$
$$3333333^2 = 11111108888889$$
$$33333333^2 = 1111111088888889$$

Fig 6

Observe this PYRAMID of THREES

A typical JAIN MATHEMATICS WORKSHEET

DIGITAL COMPRESSION OF
THE INFINITE NATURAL RINGS OF 24
designed for teenagers to discover this hidden pattern themselves!

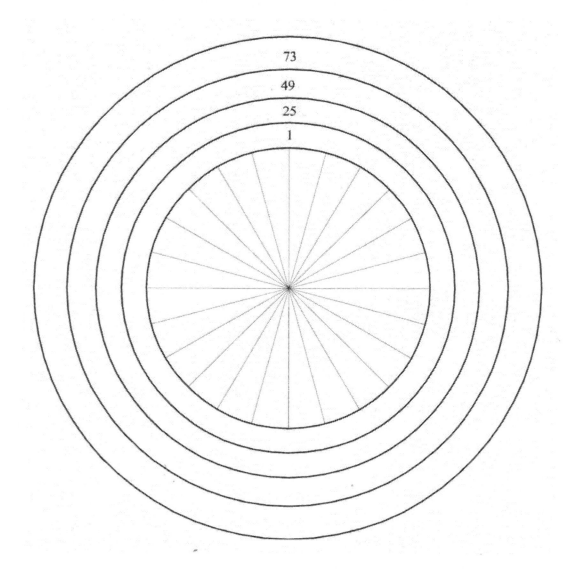

Fig 7
The natural counting Rings of 24.
Visualize the first 24 counting numbers written
clockwise in the circle, then the 2nd ring from 25 to 48,
and the 3rd ring from 49 to 72.... It will be deduced
that there is a pattern every 3 rings, but to discover this
requires the art of reducing numbers to single digits.
This evolution is shown in the next 2 diagrams.

RINGS OF 24

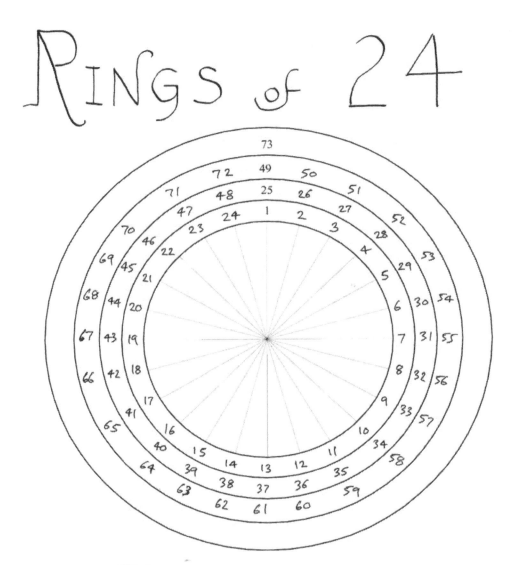

Based on the natural counting order of numbers : consecutive & sequential; ready to be reduced or compressed 2 single digits.

Fig 8
The natural counting Rings of 24 with 3 complete rings,
written circularly, like waves rippling outwardly on the surface
of a still pond when a stone is thrown,
(to illustrate how the 24 Triplets will be formed)

Compression of the first 3 Rings of 24

The Numbers from 1 to 72 have been reduced to Single Digits. These 3 Rings are repeated infinitely forming 24 Triplets that formed Ancient Musical Scales.

Fig 9

The natural counting rings of 24 with 3 complete rings,
digitally compressed to illustrate the 24 Triplets.
At the topmost north position, can you read the triplet 1-7-4?
starting from the inner ring and reading outwards.
You need to understand this to grok the following "frequencies".

The Infinite 3-6-9 Sequence formed by Compressing the Triplets in the 1ˢᵗ 3 Rings of the 24 natural counting nos.

Number of Spoke	Triplet	Compressed Triplet
1	174	1+7+4　　　　= 3
2	285	2+8+5=15=1+5 = 6
3	396	3+9+6=18=1+8 = 9
4	417	3
5	528	6
6	639	9
7	741	3
8	852	6
9	963	9
10	174	3
11	285	6
12	396	9
13	417	3
14	528	6
15	639	9
16	741	3
17	852	6
18	963	9
19	174	3
20	285	6
21	396	9
22	417	3
23	528	6
24	639	9

Sum = 144

Fig 10

The Infinite 3-6-9 Sequence Compressed from the Rings of 24 natural counting numbers, derived by isolating the 24 Triplets beginning from the Inner Ring to the Outer Ring.

DERIVATION OF THE 144 HARMONIC OF LIGHT

What is interesting here is that when we sum all the compressed digits in the far right hand column, they add up to a very important number.

We can see that there is a periodicity or repetition of 3 numbers referred to as the infinitely recursive 3-6-9 Sequence or Code. But there are 24 triplet numbers which means there are 8 x (3-6-9), thus the sum of all the digits in that column is

= 8 x (3+6+9)

= 8x18

= **144**

This is the anointed Harmonic of Light according to the works of Prof Bruce Cathie, often referred to as: The Derivation of the Harmonic Of Light 144 Code.

It is curious too that half this number arises in the fact that these infinitely repeating 3 rings of 24 contains 3 x 24 = **72** numbers.

It means that every 72 numbers, when arranged in 3 concentric rings of 24, dance with a natural rhythm with movements that are elegant and harmonic.

This is the mathematics of the future, of new age circuit boards and free energy systems.

Like the numbers 24 and 108 and 144 etc, you could write a whole book about the significance just on this sacred number 72 that relates to angles in the platonic solids and the precession of the equinoxes etc...

Both numbers 72 and 144 have a digital sum of 9.

The infinite sequence 3-6-9 has a digital sum of 9.

ISOLATING The HIDDEN 3-6-9 SEQUENCE

Radials Or spokes	The 24 Triplets From Inner Ring to Outer	Compressed Triplets To single digits	Differences between Successive Triplets
1	174	3	
2	285	6	285 - 174 = 111
3			
4			
5			
6			
7			
8			
9			
10			
11			
12			
13			
14			
15			
16			
17			
18			
19			
20			
21			
22			
23			
24			

Fig 10a
Worksheet to create The Infinite 3-6-9 Sequence
by Isolating the 24 Triplets beginning from the Inner Ring to the Outer Ring,
Analyzing the Compressed Triplets to single digits and Analyzing the
Differences between the Successive Triplets.

SOLUTION

ISOLATING THE HIDDEN 3-6-9 SEQUENCE IN THE PHI CODE			
Radials Or spokes	The 24 Triplets From Inner Ring to Outer	Compressed Triplets To single digits	Differences between Successive Triplets
1	174	3	
2	285	6	285 - 174 = 111
3	396	9	396 - 285 = 111
4	417	3	417 – 396 = 21
5	528	6	528 - 417 = 111
6	639	9	639 – 528 =111
7	741	3	741 - 639 = 102
8	852	6	852 – 741 = 111
9	963	9	963 – 852 = 111
10	174	3	963 – 174 = 789
11	285	6	285 - 174 = 111
12	396	9	396 - 285 = 111
13	417	3	417 – 396 = 21
14	528	6	528 - 417 = 111
15	639	9	639 – 528 =111
16	741	3	741 - 639 = 102
17	852	6	852 – 741 = 111
18	963	9	963 – 852 = 111
19	174	3	963 – 174 = 789
20	285	6	285 - 174 = 111
21	396	9	396 - 285 = 111
22	417	3	417 – 396 = 21
23	528	6	528 - 417 = 111
24	639	9	639 – 528 =111

Fig 10b

Solutions: Isolating the 24 Triplets beginning from the Inner Ring
to the Outer Ring. Analyzing the Compressed Triplets to single digits
to reveal the infinitely recursive 3-6-9 Pattern and analyzing
the Differences between the Successive Triplets
which reveals a high frequency of 111.

Some Questions:

Question 1 - What is the Periodicity of the Repeating Sequence as explored in the second column called: The 24 Triplets from Inner Ring to Outer. That is, what is number for the recurring cycle, or how many triplets are constantly repeating?

Question 2 - After how many concentric rings (a ring being 24 consecutive numbers) does the cycle of triplets repeat? You need to have a look again at Fig 2 to see where the obvious pattern is. Clue. Instead of the 3 rings of 24 try using 6 or 9 rings of 24 numbers and have a look at what is happening. Make sure all numbers get reduced to single digits.

Question 3 – By considering 3 concentric rings as one cycle, which is really a sequence of natural counting numbers from 1 to 3x24, what is the last or final digitally compressed number that this sequence ends on?

(Art Of Jain 1984, Amn in the Scriptorium)

SOLUTIONS + SOLFEGGIO SCALE TRIPLETS

Answer 1: Periodicity = 9

The Recurring Cycle of 9 Triplets in the Compressed Wheel of 24 Known by Musicians as part of the SOLFEGGIO SCALE								
174	285	396	417	528	639	741	852	963

Fig 10c
Solfeggio Scale generated by the same data of 24ness

Answer 2: There is a repeat or recursion every 3 concentric rings, which is what generates the triplets. As seen in Fig 10, the total sum of the compressed numbers for each 3 rings of 24 is **144**, that repeats infinitely, that is, every 3x24 or **72** successive numbers naturally compress to sums of 144.

Answer 3: The sequence of 3 concentric rings, which are the numbers from 1 to 72, starts from 1 and the cycle therefore ends on a 9 (which is the compressed form of 72 = 7+2 = 9). Nine therefore acts as a number of Completion.

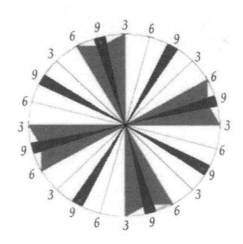

Fig 10d
The Infinitely cycling 3-6-9 Sequence creating the Harmonics of the
4th Dimensional Templar (Prime Number) Cross,
(Image taken from "Numbers Of Light" by Jason O'Hara, 2007 which deeply examines
the Mystery Of 24ness. His website is www.twentyfourthmystery.net)

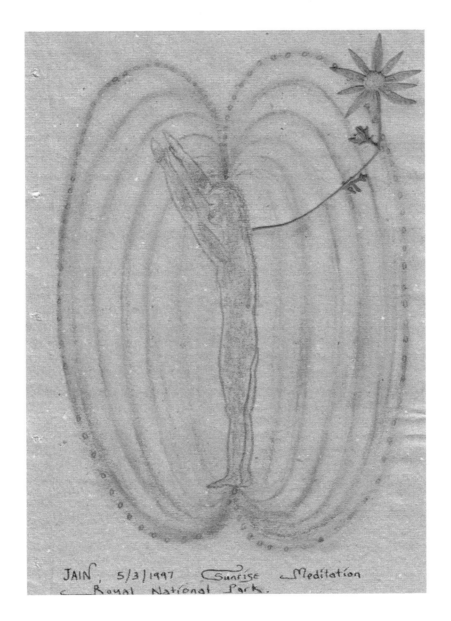

JAIN, 5/3/1997 Sunrise Meditation
Royal National Park.

Fig 10e
Art By Jain 1997
"Receiving Sunlight", fasting, feeding the toroidal auric field
surrounding the initiate, imbued by the 111 frequencies,
programming them for the higher work or service.

Remember, this is all derived from the mere counting numbers, it is not a Phi Code though it is a relative. It only gave us a clue into the mysteries of Nature or God, that there is hidden code based on 24. It begins to set the bells ringing, in fact, a whole choir or chorus of 108 bells will be tolling as the conclusion of this article, that to reveal the Phi Code, we need to grasp this understanding of 24-ness that is self-evident. That is why the ancients divided Time into 24 hours, because it is a **StarGate**.

~ CHAPTER 5 ~
JAIN'S "DOLPHUSION" MURAL

This chapter includes:

— Various Images of the Dolphusion Mural.

— 12 Essential Notes on the Dolphusion Mural:
These include: Magic Square of 3x3, The Prime Number Cross, Phi Vesica, Phi Ratio, The Arbelos, the Fractal Heart, the True Value of Pi (π), the 108 Decimals of Phi, a Root 5 Pythagorean Right-Angled Triangle, the Binary Code VW Symbol, the Atomic Structure of Platinum Crystal.

— The 3 Phi Codes in 3 Primal Languages.

 DOLPHUSION MURAL
JAIN 108

Various Images of the Dolphusion Mural

Fig A

Dolphusion Mural by Jain 108

size: 2m x 2m, oil on canvas

Fig B

The original sketch for the Dolphusion Mural, drawn by Jain 108,
originally called "F.O.X" in 1983 at Cedar Bay, far north Queensland

Fig C
Early version of the Mural of Dolphusion, by Jain, 2mx2m, oil on canvas,
not showing The 3 Phi Codes in 3 Primal Languages.

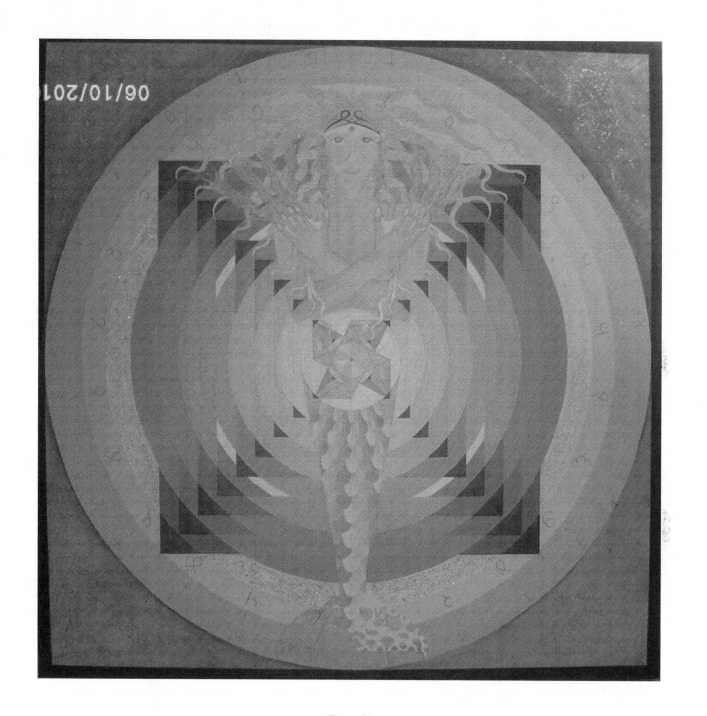

Fig D

Mural of Dolphusion, by Jain, 2mx2m, oil on canvas,

showing The 3 Phi Codes in 3 Primal Languages.

(see the next book: THE BOOK OF PHI volume 6

for a comprehensive report on the 3 Phi Codes).

12 ESSENTIAL NOTES
on the DOLPHUSION MURAL

(JAIN fasting for 2 weeks during 2010 and 2012)

This composition contains a diverse array of Sacred Sequences and geometrical symbols that have a mathematical basis or derivation.

In essence, this major mural contains all the gems as compiled in my latest book and dvd THE ART OF NUMBER, published 2012.

These include:

1 - **The MAGIC SQUARE Of 3x3** (seen at the centre of the mural, @ the belly-button point). In my other works, you can study how when the pattern of the Lo-Shu is tiled or tessellated in a certain way it produces the atomic structure of Diamond Lattice, when verified again Charles Leadbeater's work in Occult Chemistry.

The 9 numbers of Lo-Shu opens a window into the Universe's hidden architecture of Pattern. It is oldest known written down mathematics on the planet, claimed to be written in ancient Chinese text BC 2,700. It alludes both to Base 9 as the Galactic Base, and the concept of DIGITAL COMPRESSION, the process of subtracting 9 from any large number and observing it's remainder as a single digit. This is the same as adding the sums of a say a 2-digit number like 34 to get 3+4 = 7. If we were to keep subtracting 9s from 34 (where the symbol "−" means "minus") we will get the same result, check: $34 - 9 - 9 - 9 = 7$.

There are various names for this title of Digital Compression,

— Digital Reduction

— Digital Root

— Casting Out Of Nines (in Latin: Abjectio Novenaria)

— Distillation

— Digit Sums (in the Vedas this is 1 of the 16 mathematical sutras or formulae)

— Sigma Code

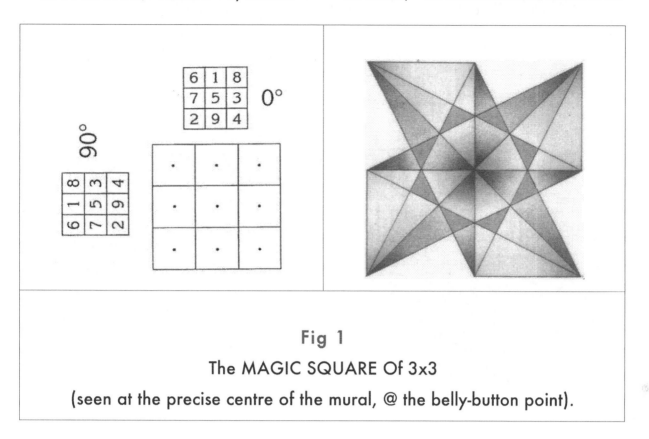

Fig 1
The MAGIC SQUARE Of 3x3
(seen at the precise centre of the mural, @ the belly-button point).

The centre of the mural is the centre of the Magic Square Yantra, it is the hara or conception point, the ability to renew or complete the karma of our many lives, and become uni-phied. I see it also as a place of Rejuvenation, the Still Point or Sweet Spot.

2 - The PRIME NUMBER CROSS or WHEEL OF 24, also emanating from the centre Point of the Mural, appearing as helicopter-like blades or wings of a dragonfly. It symbolically refers to the Dolphusion entity as having mastery of the Aerial realms (because Dolphusion, as Half-Woman, Half-Dolphin may appear limited to the realms of Water). Again, refer to the book The Art Of Number to show how the Prime Number Sequence forms this Maltese-like Cross.

(Fig 6 below, is a tribute to the Ambulance Service in Katoomba that rescued my life in 1984 when a hired thug was paid to attempt to stab me to death, lunging a knife through my heart chakra, just missing the physical heart. After an OBE Out Of Body Experience, I managed to live to tell this story, and thus these volumes of lost Phi data accessed from the realms I visited).

 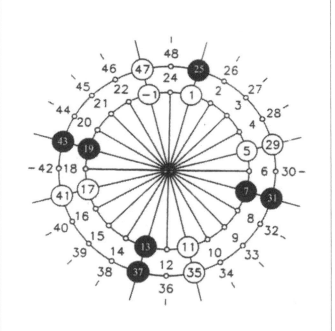

(image from the library of Peter Plichta from his book:
God's Secret Formula).

Fig 2

The Prime Number Cross based on The Wheel of 24

THE WHEEL OF 24 expresses a Time Code:

The ability to Bend Time or Time Travel. The Path to follow if you want to grok the Physics of Black Holes.

nb: the next notes spanning from 3 to 10 are all based on PHI.

3 - The **PHI VESICA** @ top left has 2 overlapping circles based on a trinitized geometrical division of the circle (meaning that the diameter of the large circle is divided into 3, such that 3 smaller circles fit inside this larger one. This magical technique opens the Door to greater revelations. The $\sqrt{5}$ geometries are revealed in a Pythagorean Triangle having the ratios of $2:3:\sqrt{5}$. (This triangle also relates to the upcoming Note No.10).

Remember that $\sqrt{5}$ is an integral part for deriving the Phi Ratio, as it's formula is $(1+\sqrt{5})\div2 = 1.618033988...$

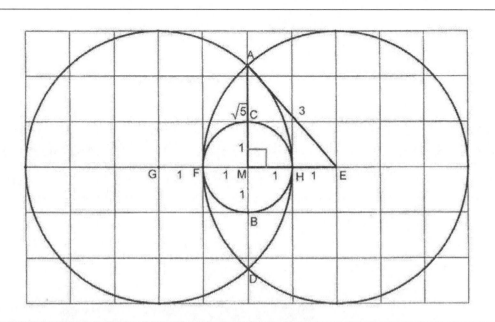

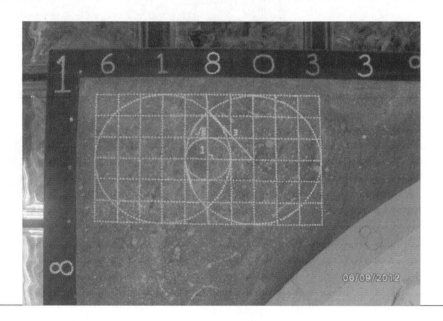

Fig 3
Phi Vesica:
The True Vesica Pisces imbued with Phi Proportions
and derived geometrically by Trinitizing the Circle.

(image originally from Hans Walser but printed in an amazing maths book
called "Glorious Golden Ratio" by Posamentier and Lehmann).

4 - The PHI RATIO "Φ" @ the top Right of the mural, geometrically expressed as a line of 55 unit's divided into it's Phi Ratio components of 21 & 34. This is the traditional standard view of expression the Golden Mean. It is really a Trinity or 3 parts. The 1st is the whole length (55), the 2nd is the longer segment (34) and the 3rd is the smaller segment. If you were to express these 3 parts another way, you could say it is a relationship of the 1ST to 2ND to the 3RD which again can be noticed as : **ST ND RD** which is really the expression of Phi Ratio as the Universal **STANDARD** of all measurements, that which is pleasing to the Eye, or beautiful.

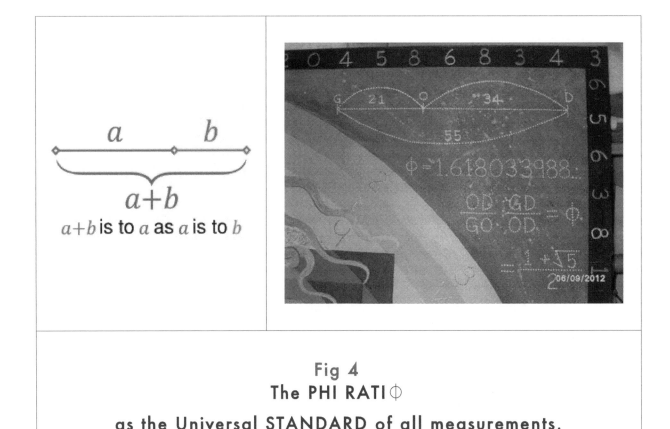

a+b is to a as a is to b

Fig 4
The PHI RATIΦ

as the Universal STANDARD of all measurements.

nb1: In my mural, the letters attributed to this trinitization of the line segment is G-O-D.

nb2: Φ (Phi) is expressed to 9 dp (Decimal Points) ie: Φ = 1.618033988...

(the 3 dots at the end "..." indicates that the number goes to infinity).

nb3: The word "GOOD" appears at the bottom of the ratios:

OD : GD = Φ

GO OD

5 - The **ARBELOS** (phi ratio of a circle like a figure 8, the phi ratio being the union of the smaller circle to the larger circle in comparison to the vertical diameter) has it's **centrepoint** at the location of my Heart, the exact position where the arms are crossed, and where I was stabbed in the Heart Chakra in 1984. Thus this is my personal Phi Centrepoint.

It is a subtle reference to my ongoing healing journey, healing the heart, and always fasting when I have approached any work upon it.

It's like a figure 8, best described as a smaller top circle and a larger lower circle, almost appearing like a snowman figure. The top circle is blue and is the aura around my head.

It is segmented so that the Wheel of 24 is pervading through, Rays 1 and 24 have not been coloured blue, as they are the rays entering my crown chakra.

The small circle is blue as it is my connection to source or spirit.

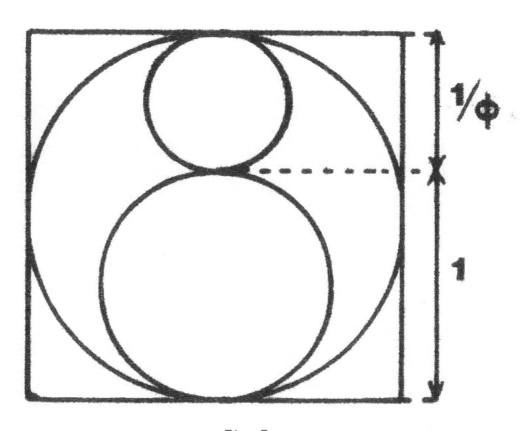

Fig 5

Arbelos of the Circle corresponds with

the Position of my heart, in the Dolphusion Mural

---

6 -
THE 3 PHI CODES or
The Three Dials Written in 3 Primal Languages

The beginning of the 3 Phi Codes is the top north or zenith point of the painting, same place where Ray 1 of the 24 rays begins, in a clockwise direction.

The beginning point is marked by a 3 petalled flower, like the fleur-de-lys, as it also represent the 3 Phi Codes that are streaming through.

— PHI CODE 1 (1,1,2) abbreviation = PC1

1, 1, 2, 3, 5, 8, 4, 3, 7, 1, 8, 9, 8, 8, 7, 6, 4, 1, 5, 6, 2, 8, 1, 9

is written on the outermost golden ring, or outer rim, in English script.

— PHI CODE 2 (1,3,4) abbreviation = PC2

1, 3, 4, 7, 2, 9, 2, 2, 4, 6, 1, 7, 8, 6, 5, 2, 7, 9, 7, 7, 5, 3, 8, 2

is written on the 2nd outermost ring, in **Arabic Script**

(nb: the numbers start from Right to Left):   ١ ٢ ٣ ٤ ٥ ٦ ٧ ٨ ٩

Fig 6a

PHI CODE 2 (1,3,4) written in Arabic Script

− PHI CODE 3 (1,4,5) abbreviation = PC3

1, 4, 5, 9, 5, 5, 1, 6, 7, 4, 2, 6, 8, 5, 4, 9, 4, 4, 8, 3, 2, 5, 7, 3

is written on the 3rd outermost golden ring, in **Devanagari Script** (modern Sanskrit).

१ २ ३ ४ ५ ६ ७ ८ ९

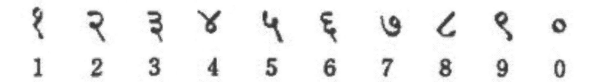

Fig 6b

PHI CODE 3 (1,4,5) written in Sanskrit/Devanagari Script

The 3 Phi Codes represent another form of the Trinity which is the essence of the Divine Proportion symbolized by the Fibonacci Sequence: 1, 1, 2, 3, 5, 8, 13 etc where 1+1 generates 2 and 2 + 3 generates 5. A trinity of numbers where the past + the present generates the future. Thus in essence, all these references to the Phi Codes and 108 Codes is really a direct connection to our DNA and to the Living Curvation of Nature's sublime Mathematics.

(Gayatri Mantra & Om)

The 3 PHI CODES
in 3 Primal Languages

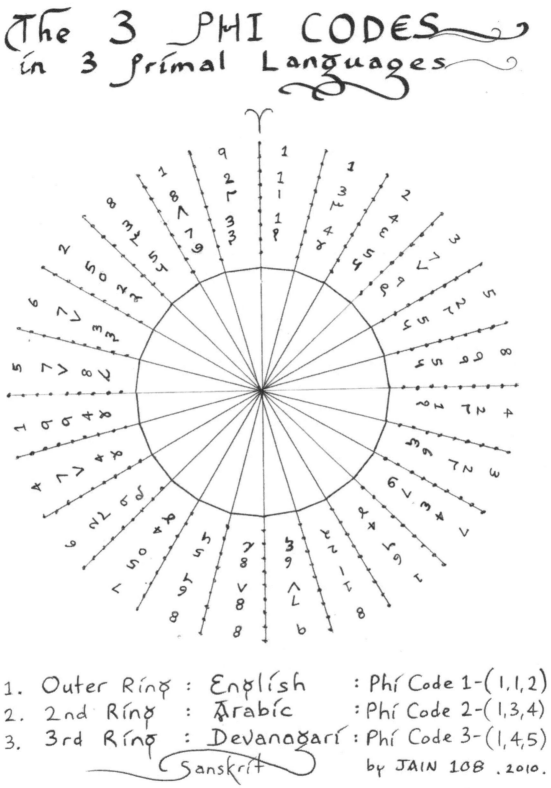

1. Outer Ring : English   : Phi Code 1 - (1,1,2)
2. 2nd Ring   : Arabic   : Phi Code 2 - (1,3,4)
3. 3rd Ring   : Devanagari : Phi Code 3 - (1,4,5)
            Sanskrit   by JAIN 108 . 2010.

Fig 6c

The 3 Phi Codes in One Wheel expressed in 3 Primal Languages:

English, Arabic and Devanagari (Sanskrit)

The 3 Phi Codes represent another form of the **Trinity** which is the essence of the Divine Proportion symbolized by the Fibonacci Sequence: 1, 1, 2, 3, 5, 8, 13 etc where 1+1 generates 2 and 2 + 3 generates 5.
A trinity of numbers where **the past + the present generates the future**.

The Pentacle embodies these numbers and their cascading ratios.

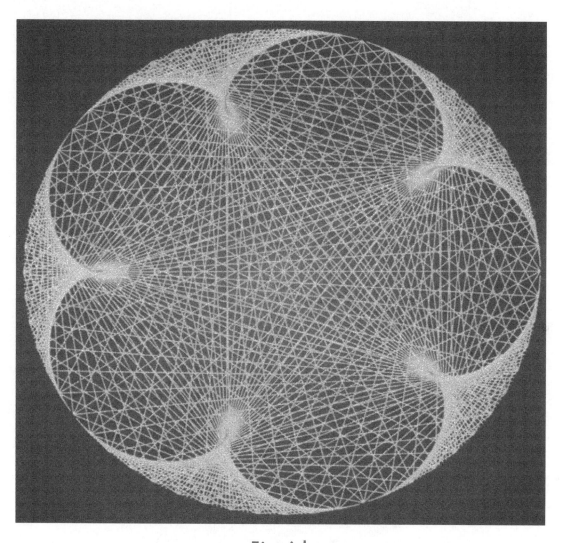

Fig 6d

Ranunculoid: An EpiCycloid with 5 cusps (n=5)
named after the buttercup flower genus Ranunculus

(image taken from: "The Universal Book Of Mathematics by David Darling")

7 - The FRACTAL HEART

This is symbolized by the necklace on the Thymus area.

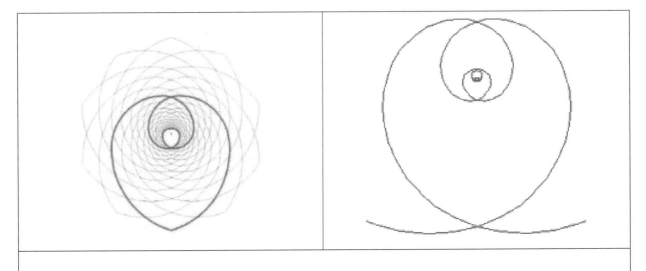

Fig 7

The Infinitely Recursive Fractal Heart:

2 Phi Spirals meeting into a Black Hole

(images courtesy from the Library of Dan Winter www.goldenmean.info).

8 - The **TRUE VALUE OF Pi (π)** = JAIN Pi = Jπ = 3.144605512...
is also expressed to 9 dp and Based on Phi.

In fact, the overall design of the mural is a large circle having a square boundary, meaning that the side of the square is really the diameter of the circle, and this is the definition of Pi. In some cultures the Circle represents the Spirit or Heaven, and the Square represents the Material World or Earth, thus the Squared Circle is unification of Heaven On Earth.

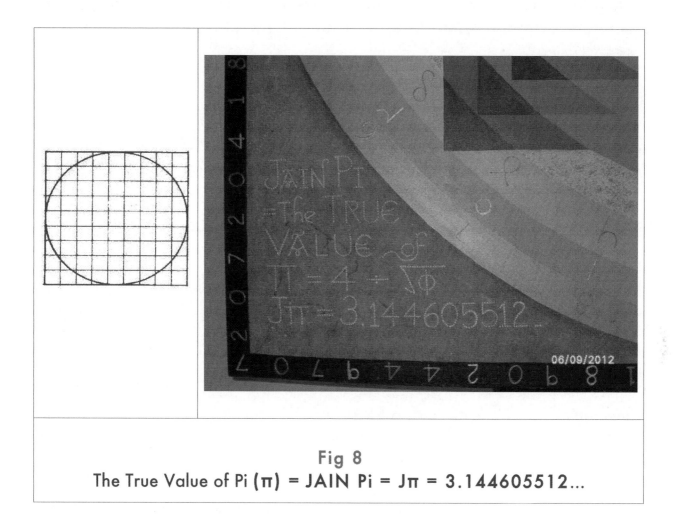

Fig 8
The True Value of Pi (π) = JAIN Pi = Jπ = 3.144605512...

This topic will be revealed in full in my forthcoming book The Book Of Phi, volume 7. It contradicts the traditional value of Pi as 3.141592... (that Pi is a Lie), and puts forward a value based on the Square Root of Phi as $4 \div \sqrt{\phi}$.

9 - THE 108 or 108+9 DECIMALS OF PHI

(from the acclaimed Golden Number Website: www.goldennumber.net.

This website also acknowledges my co-discovery of the 24 Repeating Pattern encoded in the Fibonacci Series and revealed by Digital Compression) and reveals the sum of Sri 108.

Starting from the Top Left Corner, this is seen written clockwise along the Black Square Border of the Mural: (there is a space between every tenth number for easier counting):

```
1.
6180339887  4989484820   4586834365  6381177203
0917980576  2862135448   6227052604  6281890244
9707207204  1893911374   84754088...
```

Fig 9
The Phi Ratio expressed to 108 Decimal Places

10 - A ROOT 5 PYTHAGOREAN RIGHT-ANGLED TRIANGLE

The well-known 3-4-5 Triangle is considered the 2nd most precious Gem in Mathematics (the 1st is of course the Divine Phi Proportion). It's basic principle is expressed in the note of 3 above (in the Phi Vesica information and the Root 5 Triangle is also drawn clearly). The Right Angled Triangle has the elegant proportions of **2, 3, $\sqrt{5}$**. Without knowing how to construct the Root 5 entity we could not arrive at the critical maths necessary to generate the Phi Vesica. By knowing that $\sqrt{5}$ = 2.236... to say a 1000 dp, it allows us to determine the ideal Phi Ratio as 1.618... to say a 1000 dp.

nb: this "2, 3, $\sqrt{5}$ Triangle" is taken from the previous Fig 3 (and shown again below) and is seen as AME.

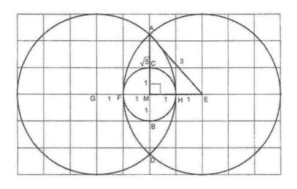

Fig 10
The "2, 3, √5 Triangle" (AME)
extracted from the previous Fig 3 (Phi Vesica).

11 - The BINARY CODE VW SYMBOL

The VW symbol is seen @ the bottom right, above my signature (Jain 1999). It is really The Circle of 9 expressed here to illuminate that Base 9 is a key to understanding the Mysteries.

(image on left is taken from the works of Marko Rodin of Aerodynamics and Vortex Based Mathematics).

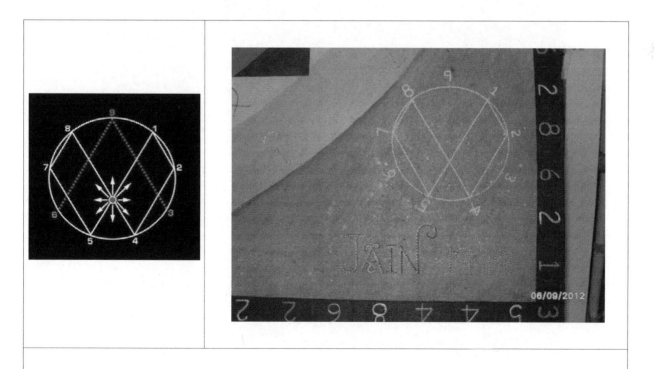

Fig 11
The Binary Code VW Symbol emblematic of Galactic Base 9

12 - The ATOMIC STRUCTURE OF PLATINUM CRYSTAL Derived From the VISUAL MULTIPLICATION TABLE

nb: This image has not yet been added to the mural, it is essentially one of the important psycho-Active diagrams that is a good candidate to be painted in reference to the fact that it is based on Digital Compression and Base 9, obeying the essential theme: Translating Number Into Atomic Art.

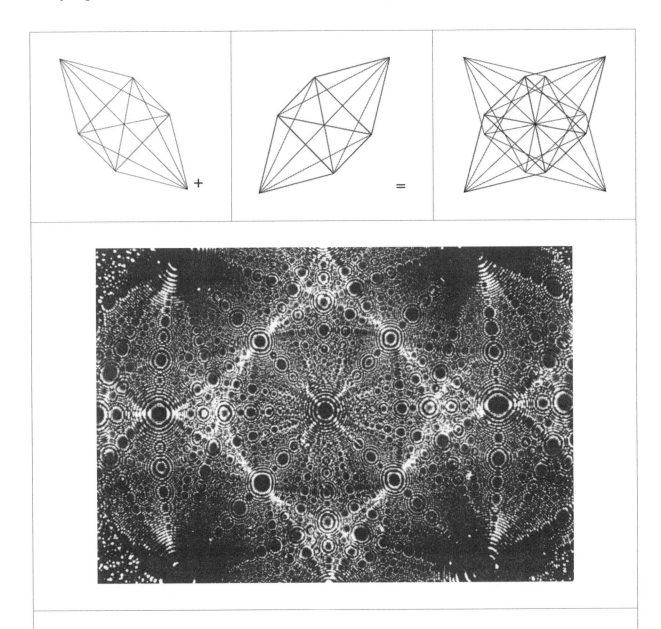

Fig 12
The Atomic Structure of Rutile Crystal (top left)

and Atomic Structure of Platinum Crystal (main central image)

Derived From the Visual (or Digitally Compressed) Multiplication Table.

(image courtesy of the late Professor Mueller, reprinted in The Keys of Enoch by J.J Hurtak).

~ CHAPTER 6 ~
APPENDICES

Chapter Contents Includes:

Appendix 1
- The Mathematical Laws that Define a True Phi Code 108

Appendix 2
- Phi Code 1, 2 and 3 Linked to the Cuboctahedron: - Signature of 6-6-6-6

Appendix 3
- Phi-Binary Questions That Arise

Appendix 4
- Some Questions That Arise.
  - Is there a 3-6-3-6-3-6 Hexagon Pattern?
  - Connection to DNA Base Pairs

Appendix 5
- The 24-Cell And How It Relates To The Phi Code

Appendix 6
- Powers of Phi Based on Multiplication & Addition

Appendix 7
- Chart of the Powers of Phi

Appendix 8
- Bibliography + Internet Sites Referenced

~ APPENDIX 1 ~

THE MATHEMATICAL LAWS THAT DEFINE A TRUE PHI CODE 108

As we go deeper into this field, we must start writing down the mathematical laws that define various Phi Codes.

eg: **A true Phi Code, has in it's 2x12 Array, 11 Columns or Pairs of numbers that sum to 9.**

Another way of saying this, is that **the sum of all 24 Digitally Compressed Single Digits must sum to 117** (being 108+9 or 13x9).

This is a basic tenet, a truth, a veritable Law of Numbers.

Another basic tenet, is that each Phi Code has 4 Hexagonal Relationships, meaning that at every 4th digit, there is a sophisticated and intelligent hexagonal pattern that defines counter-rotating binary patterns, Pairing Patterns as in either 1&8, meaning: 1-8-1-8-1-8 or 2&7 or 4&5.

Why are there only 3 such hexagonal pairs, not 4?

An anomaly arises: Another question must be asked:

Up to this moment, I have not found a Phi Code that has a hexagonal pairing of 3&6. (The 3-6-9 Missing or Gap Sequence is Tesla's critical secret).

I believe it is through these **anomalies** that true wisdom is found, as it creates perseverance, develops the intuition, and keeps us probing for nature's symmetry.

And why are there only 3 primitive or basic Phi Codes, not 4?

Perhaps it's a fanciful notion, that if there were 4 distinct Phi Codes, with 4 distinct hexagonal pairing systems that run through the labyrinth of all the other possible Phi Code variations or permutations, that this would then relate obviously to the 4 DNA molecular bases (T-A-G-C) that are also paired systems: Thymine always pairs with Adenine (T-A) and Guanine always pairs with Cytosine (G-C).

~ APPENDIX 2 ~

PHI CODE 1, 2 & 3
LINKED TO THE CUBOCTAHEDRON
- SIGNATURE OF 6 – 6 – 6 – 6

On the Nature of the 3 Phi Codes plugged into the Wheel of 24, what is distinctly seen are 4 hexagons, see Fig 2b below. We must therefore ask ourselves, where in Nature or Science do we see 4 Hexagons contained in one Circle or Sphere.

The only magical shape that I know that is composed of 4 hexagonal rings is the alchemical CubOctaHedron. If you were to hold this shape in your hands, and the size is that of the an orange, you could comfortably circle your fingers, using both thumb and middle-fingers, to trace the 4 equatorial and hexagonal pathways. These 4 hex rings lie on the path of the 4 Great Circles around the Sphere.

You can see these 4 hex rings in this figure below, the CubOctaHedron, one of the 13 Archimedean or Semi-Regular Solids.

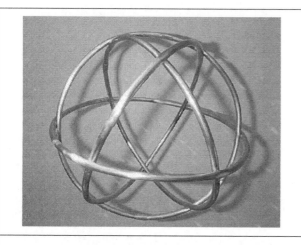 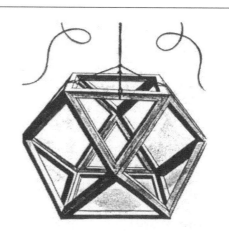

Fig 2a

The Cuboctahedron has 4 Hexagonal rings that make it appear as having 6 Square and 8 Triangular faces.   (image on right by Leonardo da Vinci).

So here it is, we found a distinct, intelligent and sophisticated and concatenating link with 2 apparently different geometrical topics, that of the Phi Code 108 Mysteries and the Archimedean Solid CubOctaHedron.

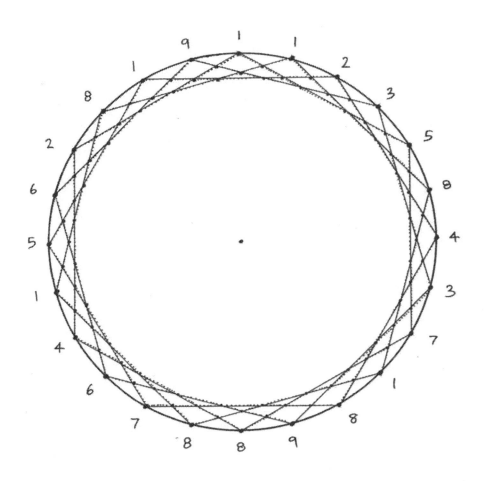

The 4 Hexagonal Arrangements
that exist inherently in PHI CODE 1.
Phi Codes 2 + 3 also demonstrate this.

Fig 2b

The 4 various Hexagonal Arrangements that exist inherently

inside the circularized Phi Code 1 Pattern.

In a sense, it has a symbolic meaning

or signature of **6-6-6-6**.

~ APPENDIX 3 ~

PHI–BINARY QUESTIONS THAT ARISE

The discovery of the Counter-Rotating Binary hexagons in the 3 Phi Code 108 circular arrangements leads us to contemplate an important realization and ask some serious questions.

Are we of the same make-up as are computers?

Said another way: Is there a direct link between the BIOLOGICAL (Phi Codes) and DIGITAL AGE (Binary Code)?

Are we meant to embrace, honour the God of Tech as a part of our Being or Oneness?

Can Robots therefore have and demonstrate Consciousness?

Are we Borg in Nature?

Is this why the racing-car driver becomes One with his-her Machine?

How can this be, that the very Mathematics of the Doubling Sequence and of our Mitotic embryonic development, be embedded or wedded to the very Mathematics of Living Curvation, of Flowers and Stars!

~ APPENDIX 4 ~
SOME QUESTIONS THAT ARISE
- Is there a 3-6-3-6-3-6 Hexagon Pattern?
- Connection to DNA Base Pairs

There are many other questions that need to be asked and solved.

I will conclude this chapter with a typical one of these questions that need to be investigated for further research.

Question:

Is there a 3-6-3-6-3-6 Hexagon Pattern that arises in any of the known or unknown Phi Code 108 Patterns?

Answer:

At the moment, in this booklet, we have discovered distinct hexagon arrangements in the circularized phi codes, that have the 1-8-1-8-1-8 and the

7-2-7-2-7-2 and the 4-5-4-5-4-5 patterns.

There is an obvious Pairing system summing to 9.

3 Pairs is fine, but what if there was a 4th Pair? If there is another one, that would confirm that there exist 4 distinct Pairing systems, complementary in nature and harmonically associated to Galactic Base 9ness. It would indeed have a reference to the 4 DNA bases T-A-G-C that know how to pair themselves Thymine links with Adenine, and Guanine links with Cytosine in their molecular dance.

As explored earlier, the 3-6-9 symbolism is a Gap Sequence, in terms of fibonaccoid sequences, whenever we add a 3 or 6 or 9 to a sequence starting with "3" we only keep getting triplet permutations of 3-6-9. So fact would confirm that there is not a 4th hexagonal sequence in the order of 3-6-3-6-3-6.

Marko Rodin has spent his life examining this gap sequence of 3-6-9 which are the 3 numbers absent in the Doubling Binary Sequence: 1-2-4-8-16-32-64 etc which reduces to a digitally reduced Binary Code of 1-2-4-8-7-5 having a periodicity of 6 repeating single digits.

DNA Base Pairs

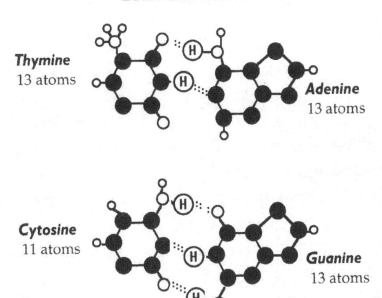

Fig 4a

The 4 Genetic bases and how they link in Pairs.

(Taken from: Katya Walter's book: "Tao Of Chaos" sub-titled: DNA and the I-Ching)

What is of interest here is the internal zipper of **Hydrogen Bonding**, which have been confirmed to be in the **golden mean** or **phi ratio**...

The overall penta-hexa arrangement of molecules is the similar structure to many other psychedelic substances like psyillocibin (of magic mushrooms), DMT, ayahusca etc, even coffee is penta-hexa!

The above diagram is also indicative how Nature chooses Paired systems to store data. This "pairing" relates to our mathematical enquiry of the 3 Phi Codes as they also are Paired Systems (that sum to 9).

~ APPENDIX 5 ~

THE 24-CELL AND HOW IT RELATES TO THE PHI CODE

by JAIN 108

In this section, we are interested in knowing which shapes, whether they be 2-dimensional, or 3-dimensional or even 4-dimensional, that can exist to contain or hold vibrationally, or embed, this curious 24-ness of the Phi Codes.

We saw in my previous books, that the only Platonic Solid that has 24 Faces and 24 Edges, is the Star Tetrahedron.

Fig 5a
The 24 faces and 24 edges of the Star Tetrahedron

Well, there happens to be another shape, that has 24 faces and 24 Vertices (points that touch the sphere). And it also has 24 octahedral faces! This amazing shape is called the "24 Cell" and exists as a 4th Dimensional shape.

Fig 5b
The 24-Cell, having 24 faces and 24 vertices and 24 octahedra.
This 24-Cell is also known as The Hyper-Diamond
or IcosiTetraChoron.
(image taken from John Baez's site "Platonic Solids In All Dimensions"
http://www.math.ucr.edu/home/baez/platonic.html)

How to visualize it.

Visualize a cube, and from the centre of the 6 faces, push in the middle of each face, making dents to form 6 inverted pyramids. Keep pushing these inverted pyramids until all of these pyramids meet at the cube's centre.

(This is the opposite principle of "stellating" a platonic or archimedian solid or shape, rather than gluing pyramids or star-like shapes to expand the original form, we are going in, not exploding, but imploding).

At this point, it is tempting to fill up those 6 imploded pyramid dents with the shape that almost fit's perfectly inside of them. We choose the Octahedron. These 6 regular octahedra do not fit exactly the vessel described, if they did, they would have the magical quality of tiling space in 3-dimensions using octahedra, 6 meeting at each vertex. Since they do not fit exactly, we cheat a little bit, to make them fit, by wiggling them or curling up the pattern into the 4th dimension to arrive at a shape known as a 4th dimensional polytope, we call this one the "24-Cell" for short, it has 24 octahedral faces, with 6 meeting at each vertex. It has 3 Octahedra meeting to an edge, and also has 96 edges. It is one

of six possible 4th Dimensional shapes known as the 6 Regular Polychora.
Of distinction, is the important fact that **the 24-Cell is Self-Dual**, and has no direct 3-Dimensional analog. This is quite interesting, **when a shape is transfigured, and still becomes itself, implies that it has universal properties, or timeless principles based on eternal, fixed design.** Is not a seed self-dual, in the sense that something is sprouted to become itself?

According to Coxeter, in 1969 who analysed this shape, to construct this 24-Cell using co-ordinates of (K1, K1, 0, 0) and to measure the vertices means we have a circum-radius of Root 2 (=1.4142...), and edge length of Root 2. This means that there are 4 distinct non-zero distances between the vertices of the 24-Cell in 4-Space.

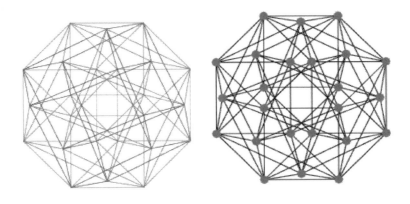

Fig 5c
The 96 edges of the 24-Cell can be partitioned
into 3 HyperCubes or Tesseracts
(images of Figs 3 and 4 are taken from an excellent site called
Wolfram MathWorld": http://mathworld.wolfram.com/24-Cell.html)

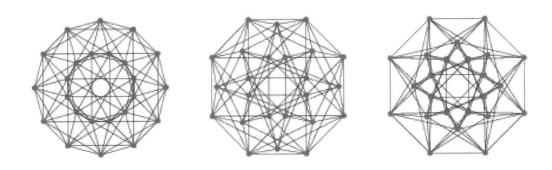

Fig 5d
The skeleton maps of the 24-Cell

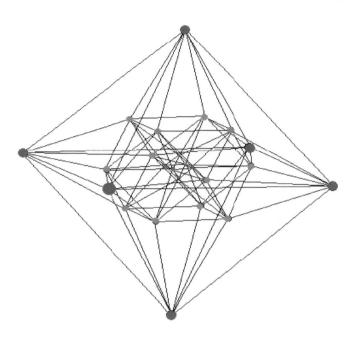

Fig 5e
Another perspective of the 24-Cell aka Hyper-Diamond

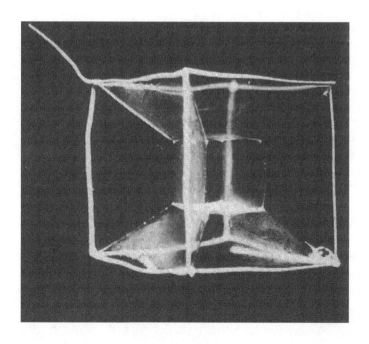

Fig 5e
This wire-framed Soap Bubble, showing a smaller cube within the larger cube is
a good example of what Fourth Dimension means, what Fractal means, when
the small picture is the same as the large picture,
when THE INSIDE IS THE SAME AS THE OUTSIDE.

~ APPENDIX 6 ~

POWERS OF PHI BASED ON MULTIPLICATION AND ADDITION

(Taken from: http://www.vashti.net/mceinc/derivphi.htm)

DERIVE PHI EXACTLY

Once you know that

phi + 1 = phi * phi

(where "phi" = 1.618...   and the asterisk "*" means "Multiplication").
You can apply simple **Algebra** and find the actual value of **phi**. This was the gift of the Arabs, they invented this thing called "x" to represent The Unknown, and after some fancy footwork, they arrived at the Known, making the Invisible Visible. Without this algebra, we could not determine the value of Phi to be 1.618033988...

First, combine and rearrange the terms to form a standard quadratic equation:

$$phi^2 - phi - 1 = 0$$

Not too bad so far.

Now we can use the **Quadratic Formula** to solve for phi.

The Quadratic Formula says that when you have a standard quadratic equation, like this:

$$ax^2 + bx + c = 0$$

then you can find the value of **x** from the values of **a**, **b**, and **c**, like so:

$$x = \frac{-b \pm \sqrt{b^2 - 4ac}}{2a}$$

Going back to our equation for **phi**

$$phi^2 - phi - 1 = 0$$

we get these values for **a**, **b**, and **c**:

a = 1

b = -1

c = -1

Plugging into the Quadratic Formula gives:

$$phi = \frac{-(-1) \pm \sqrt{(-1)^2 - 4(1)(-1)}}{2(1)}$$

$$= \frac{1 \pm \sqrt{1 + 4}}{2}$$

$$= \frac{1 \pm \sqrt{5}}{2}$$

Your pocket calculator, computer, or slide rule can tell you, with varying degrees of accuracy, that the precise value of the square root of 5 is (approximately)

2.23606797749 97...

So that we get:

$$\frac{1 + 2.2360679774997...}{2} \implies 1.61803398874989...$$

and
(remember a square root has two values, one positive and one negative)

$$\frac{1 - 2.2360679774997...}{2} \implies -0.61803398874989...$$

This is puzzling.

The first number makes sense, because we know that the number we're looking for is bigger than one and greater than zero, that being in the nature of **growth** (things get **larger** when you multiply by **phi**). But when you've finished unfolding the **Golden Rectangle**, and you go **backwards** towards the origin, things are getting **smaller** and moving in the **opposite direction**. That's when you meet this unexpected alter ego of **phi**.

Hmmm... We got here because, if you **add one to phi you get phi squared**. What happens if we **subtract** one from **phi**? Well, multiply by -1 and you've got this same inverted side of **phi**, once again moving backwards and down towards the Cosmic Navel.

We know that **phi** somehow embodies both addition and multiplication.

By the way, if

$$1 + phi = phi^2$$

then what does this equal?

$$phi + phi^2 = ?$$

How about this?

$$phi^4 + phi^5 = ?$$

Or, for that matter?

phi^{499} $+ phi^{500}$ $= $?

The answers are phi^3 and phi^6 and phi^{501}

What we've stumbled onto here is the mathematically perfect parallel of the Fibonacci series we started out with. If you recall, a Fibonacci series is defined by each successive term being the sum of the previous two. So if you start out with one and **phi**, you get:

1, phi, (phi + 1), (phi + (phi + 1)), ((phi + 1) + (phi + (phi + 1))), ...

Or, as we just saw:

1,   phi, phi^2, phi^3, phi^4, phi^5 etc

Each term in these two series is equivalent. For instance:

1 = 1

phi = phi

phi^2 = (1 + phi)

phi^3 = (phi + (1 + phi))

phi^4 = ((1 + phi) + (phi + (1 + phi)))   and so on.

Notice that each power of **phi** can be calculated by addition. There is absolutely no multiplication required! This time there's no approximation; each successive term in the series is *exactly* the sum of the two previous two terms and at the same time is *exactly* the previous term multiplied by **phi**.

The Caduceus
is the true and
original symbol for
the Medical services, and
it's meaning is derived from
the Powers Of Phi 1.618033.....
continually multiplying itself to
bridge the dimensions from the atomic
to galactic. Unfortunately, over the century,
Big Pharma alligned with other other Big companies
like Big Oil, Big Guns (military) and Big Ag (Monsanto) have
pathetically tried to claim this most ancient and powerful
symbol but can not succeed as people all over the world
realize that chemo-therapies are deliberate poisons
culling our muggle populations, but people are
slowly beginning to wake and demand natural
safe therapies based on plants and light.
This book therefore is about ushering
in this true galactic mathematics.

Fig6a
Caduceus symbol of Powers Of Phi
aka Stairway To Heaven
aka Jacob's Ladder.

~ APPENDIX 7 ~
CHART OF THE POWERS OF PHI

0.090	0.146	0.236	0.382	0.618	1.000	1.618	2.618	4.236	6.854	11.090
ϕ^{-5}	ϕ^{-4}	ϕ^{-3}	ϕ^{-2}	ϕ^{-1}	ϕ^{0}	ϕ^{1}	ϕ^{2}	ϕ^{3}	ϕ^{4}	ϕ^{5}

$\phi^1 =$

1.61803398874989484820458683436563811772 03091798057628621354486227052604628189O

phi to the power of (1/2) = 1.272019649514069 to 15 dp
(is the same as the Square Root of 1.618...).
On a calculator you would type:
pow(1.618033988749895,(1/2)) ' square root of Phi

****

.618033988749895 squared

= .381966011250105

= reciprocal of Phi squared

= (1/Phi)^2 or

= (1/Φ)^2

~ APPENDIX 8 ~
— BIBLIOGRAPHY —

- THE ART OF NUMBER by **Jain 108**, published 2012

- GLORIOUS GOLDEN RATIO by **Posamentier** and **Lehmann,** 2012 (p129)

- THE KEYS OF ENOCH by **J.J. Hurtak**

- AERODYNAMICS AND VORTEX BASED MATHEMATICS by **Marko Rodin** (see 139)

- GOD'S SECRET FORMULA by **Peter Plichta,** (p128)

- THE UNIVERSAL BOOK OF MATHEMATICS by **David Darling**

- THE POET PRINCE by **Kathleen McGowan**.

- SPIRAL SYMMETRY by Editors **Istvan Hargittai** and **Clifford A. Pickover**.
  (Computer Generated Sunflower. Jain's Emblem for the New One World Flag. See p51. Image referencing: Robert Dixon's work. Also used as main pattern for front cover).

- TAO OF CHAOS (sub-titled: DNA and the I-CHING) by **Katya Walter** (p147)

INTERNET SITES REFERENCED

- http://www.vashti.net/mceinc/derivphi.htm
  (for Powers Of Phi Based On Multiplication & Addition)

- http://www.math.ucr.edu/home/baez/platonic.html
  (image of the 24 Cell taken from John Baez's site "Platonic Solids In All Dimensions")

- www.theResonanceProject.com
  (Nassim Haramein: everything is a Torus from protons, apples to planets and suns)

- www.twentyfourthmystery.net
  (Jason O'Hara, 2007, "Numbers Of Light")

- www.goldenmean.info
  (Dan Winter (see p136)

- http://GoldenNumber.net/PhiFormulaGeometry.htm
  (see p138 on108 Decimals of Phi), +
  (diagram of Phi derived geometrically by Bengt Erik Erlandsen)

- http://mathworld.wolfram.com/24-Cell.html
  (for "Wolfram MathWorld")

- http://www.math.ucr.edu/home/baez/platonic.html
  (image on p147 taken from John Baez's site:
  "Platonic Solids In All Dimensions" + see pp150-151)

~ CHAPTER 7 ~

INDEX

I N D E X + Number Harmonics + Sequences

nb: any page numbers <u>underlined</u> means that this reference is an **image** or a **chart**, not text.

LEGEND:
- "aka" means "Also Known As".
- "Ch" means "Chapter".
- "MSq" means "Magic Square".

THIS INDEX CONTAINS 3 PARTS:
- INDEX OF WORDS
- INDEX OF NUMBERS
- INDEX OF DIGITALLY COMPRESSED SEQUENCES

Art by Jain, 1999, Mural of Hathor, oil on canvas,

(a 4th Dimensional Venusian, cow-earred being; a sonic and frequency master).

INDEX OF WORDS

INDEX
OF
NUMBERS

aka HARMONICS INDEX

aka NUMERICAL DICTIONARY Of NUMBER REFERENCES

aka HARMONIC STAIRWAY

nb: Any reference to an image or chart is underlined.

LEGEND:

... (3 Dots) after some numbers means that the decimal keeps on continuing.

: (Colon) means Proportion, as is 21:34, spoken as "the ratio of 21 to 34".

–0.618033... – 153-154 (algebraic root of the phi formula generates a minus or negative value "–"),

0 – 76 (decimal repetition of Zeroes and Nines),

.0069444... – 45 (Derivation of Harmonic 144),

.142857 – 101 (Enneagram and Division of Circle into 7), 103-104 (fraction for 1/7), 106-109 (in Enneagram),

.285714 – 104 (decimal form answer for 2/7 pronounced .285714 repeater...),

.333... – 104 (decimalization of the fraction 1/3 for circle divided into 3),

.618... – (Reciprocal of "Phi" and expressed as "phi")

.666... – 104 (decimalization of the fraction 2/3 for circle divided into 3),

.999... – 104 (decimalization of the fraction 3/3 for circle divided into 3),

1 – 66 (& Reciprocal of Phi),

1.272... – 11 (Square Root Of Phi), 47 (Squaring of Circle), 48-49 (Squaring of Circle), 137 (True Value of Pi in Dolphusion Mural),

1.414... (Square root of 2) – 150 (Coxeter on the 24 Cell),

1.618033988... (Phi) – 9-11, etc referenced throughout the whole book.

1.732... (root of 3) –

60 — 46 (Time),

64 — 47 (Proportion of 8:9 in Squaring of the Circle),

72 — 54 (Angelic Names of God), 95 (degrees in SpiralLateral), 115 (numbers in 3 Rings of 24), 119,

81 — 47 (Proportion of 8:9 in Squaring of the Circle),

90° — 138-139 (Root 5 Pythagorean Right-Angled Triangle + Phi Vesica),

96 — 150-151 (sides in the Self-Dual 24 Cell),

111 — 117 (Differences between most of the Successive Triplets in the Rings of 24),

108 — 13 (segments of Circle), 26, 35-37 (Worksheets), 45-46 (Double 108 forming the 216 Harmonic), 46-47 (Binary of 27), 61 (Hertz), 138 (108 Decimals of Phi),

108+9 — 54 (the 72 Angelic Names of God and the 3 Phi Codes), 110 (Pyramid of 3ness), 138 (108 Decimals of Phi),

117 — 54 (the 72 Angelic Names of God and the 3 Phi Codes), 142,

144 — 45 (Derivation of Harmonic 144), 115-118 (Rings of 24),

147 — 57 (Solfeggio Scale Triplet in PC2 as a 3x8 Matrix),

216 — 13 (Harmonic), 45,

222 — 57 (Solfeggio Scale Triplet in PC2 as a 3x8 Matrix),

258 — 57 (Solfeggio Scale Triplet in PC2 as a 3x8 Matrix),

285 — 57 (Solfeggio Scale Triplet in PC2 as a 3x8 Matrix),

369 — 57 (Solfeggio Scale Triplet in PC2 as a 3x8 Matrix),

417 — 57 (Solfeggio Scale Triplet in PC2 as a 3x8 Matrix),

432 — 46-47 (Binary of 27),

695 — 45 (Derivation of Harmonic 144),

777 — 57 (Solfeggio Scale Triplet in PC2 as a 3x8 Matrix),

864 — 46 (Harmonic Of Time), 47 (Binary of 27),

963 — 57 (Solfeggio Scale Triplet in PC2 as a 3x8 Matrix),

1,089 — 101, 110 (Pyramid of 3ness),

1,728 — 46-47 (Binary of 27),

3,456 — 46-47 (Binary of 27),

86,400 — 46 (Seconds in a Day),

864,000 — 46 (Diameter of Sun),

999,999 — 103 (=142857 x 7 (relating to the decimalized fraction for 1/7),

INDEX
OF DIGITALLY COMPRESSED SEQUENCES

("P" = Periodicity = How many numbers in that Sequence)

1, 1, 2, 3, 5, 8, 4, 3, 7, 1, 8, 9, 8, 8, 7, 6, 4, 1, 5, 6, 2, 8, 1, 9
[Phi Code 1: (1,1,2) The Compression of the primal Fibonacci Sequence; The 1st of the 3 possible Dials. P=24]

1, 2, 3, 4, 5, 6, 7, 8, 9
(Digitally Compressed 1x Times Table. P=9)

1, 2, 4, 8, 7, 5
(Binary Code. P=6)

1, 2, 6, 3, 6, 6, 9
(Digitally Compressed Sequence of Phibonacci Products, from a previous book on phi. P=7)

1, 3, 4, 7, 2, 9, 2, 2, 4, 6, 1, 7, 8, 6, 5, 2, 7, 9, 7, 7, 5, 3, 8, 2
[Phi Code 2 PC2: (1,3,4): – The Powers Of Phi 108) The Compression of another Fibonacci Sequence; The 2nd of the 3 possible Dials. P=24]

1 – 4 – 2 – 2 – 4 – 1 – 8 – 5 – 7 – 7 – 5 – 8
(Phi Code 2 or PC2: (1,3,4): The Alternate Pairs or Every 2nd Number of the Lucas Sequence, see p55)

1, 4, 5, 9, 5, 5, 1, 6, 7, 4, 2, 6, 8, 5, 4, 9, 4, 4, 8, 3, 2, 5, 7, 3
[Phi Code 3: PC3: (1,4,5) The Compression of another Fibonacci Sequence; The 3rd of the 3 possible Dials. P=24]

1, 4, 9, 7, 7, 9, 4, 1, 9
[from the n^2 = (Squared Numbers Sequence):
1, 4, 9, 16, 25, 36, 49, 64, 81, 100, 121, 144... P=9]

1 – 8 – 1 – 8 – 1 – 8
(1 of 3 distinct Hexagonal Pattern in the 3 Circularized Phi Codes. see p146-147)

1, 8, 9
[from the n^3 = (Cubic Numbers Sequence):
1, 8, 27, 64, 125, 216, 343, 512, 729, 1000... P=3]

2, 4, 6, 8, 1, 3, 5, 7, 9
(Digitally Compressed 2x Times Table. P=9)

2 – 7 – 2 – 7 – 2 – 7
(1 of 3 distinct Hexagonal Pattern in the 3 Circularized Phi Codes. see p146-147)

3 – 3 – 9 – 6 – 6 – 9
(Digitally Compressed Pattern in all 3 Phi Codes, being the 4th number of each Phi Code.
See p102)

3, 6, 3, 6, 3, 6
(146-147 Hexagon Pattern. This sequence does not exist. see pp 8)

3, 6, 9
(Digitally Compressed 3x Times Table. P=3) (see p5) +
(Pattern in the 3 Phi Codes, see Ch 4 on p101, p107-109 & 111-118 Rings of 24), p142,
146-147)

3 – 7 – 9 – 2 – 6 – 7 – 6 – 2 – 9 – 7 – 3 – 2
(Phi Code 2 or PC2: (1,3,4):
The Alternate Pairs or Every 2nd Number of the Lucas Sequence, see p55)

4 – 5 – 4 – 5 – 4 – 5
(1 of 3 distinct Hexagonal Pattern in the 3 Circularized Phi Codes.
see p146-147)

4, 8, 3, 7, 2, 6, 1, 5, 9
(Digitally Compressed 4 Times Table). P=9

5, 1, 6, 2, 7, 3, 8, 4, 9
(Digitally Compressed 5x Times Table. P=9)

6, 3, 9
(Digitally Compressed 6x Times Table. P=3)

6, 6, 6, 6
(see pages 143-144), being a signature for 4 various Hexagonal Arrangements that exist
inherently inside the circularized Phi Code 1 Pattern)

7 – 3 – 1 – 5 – 5 – 0 – 5 – 5 – 1 – 3 – 7 – (5)
(Phi-Prime Connection, Palindromic Sequence. see pp33-34
This is derived from the differences between each of the 12 Pairs in PC2)

7, 5, 3, 1, 8, 6, 4, 2, 9
(Digitally Compressed 7x Times Table. P=9)

7 – 7 – 5 – 3 – 1 – 7 – 1 – 3 – 5 – 7 – 7 – 0
(differences between each of the 12 Pairs in PC1. See p44)

8, 7, 6, 5, 4, 3, 2, 1, 9
(Digitally Compressed 8x Times Table. P=9)

9, 9, 9
(the Binary Code cut in half and Pairs adding to 9. See p103)

12:24:60
(Time Code of the Fibonacci Sequence)

"ODD, ODD, EVEN"
(Pattern in the Lucas Sequence "24 Repeating Pattern", aka Powers Of PHI. see p63 et al)

...finis...

BACK COVER BLURB

This most rare book of ancient knowledge will inspire you to appreciate the Powers of Phi (Φ): the ratio of 1:1.618033... continually multiplying by itself. When all these Powers are rounded off to the nearest whole number, and **Digital Compression** is applied to this Sequence to reduce large digits to single digits, what appears is an **infinitely Repeating 24 Pattern** that magically adds up to **108** (worshipped in the Vedas). I call it **Phi Code 2 (1,3,4)**. This great body of knowledge, for the first time ever published, constitutes the second of the **3 primal Phi Codes or ParaPhysical Dials** (that all sum to 108). Learn how the **Infectivity** of these 3 Phi Codes generate **72 distinct triplet permutations**. In fact, any two numbers in the universe, when added together in such a Fibonaccoid style, resolve to 1 of these 3 primal Phi Codes, each being an infinitely repeating 24 Pattern, adding to 108.

This compendium will teach you in depth knowledge on:

- **The Phi Ratio 1:1.618033** (the Living Curvation or Mathematics of Nature as seen in Pine Cones and Sunflowers etc)
- The anointed Number 108. Why are more than a billion Hindu people on the planet mindlessly worshipping "**Shri 108**"?
- The ubiquitous Number 72. Why did the ancient seers describe in full detail the **72 Angelic Names of God**?
- The **Number Bases of 9** and **12** as Star-Gates
- The **Wheel of 24** and Phi-ometry
- The **Fibonacci Sequence (1,1,2)** and **Lucas Sequence (1,3,4)**
- **Prime Numbers** and how they are embedded in the Phi Codes
- **Solfeggio Scales** and Mathematical Trinities
- The **3-6-9 Code** referenced by Nikola Tesla (paraphrased: "...whoever understands the meaning of 3-6-9 will understand the Universe and Free Energy...")
- The Winged Medical Symbol (**Caduceus** with intertwining snakes) and how we the people can reclaim it from the claws of Big Pharma. This **Stairway to Heaven** or **Jacob's Ladder** is the symbol for the Powers of Phi
- The secret of **Digital Compression**, without which none of the above could be revealed! These Vectors of Transmission have a Universal Language based on the numbers for Zero to 9. You will see why they do not teach this "modulus 9" at schools, as it truly opens the doorway into the Phi Mysteries.
- and much more...

Mural by Jain, 1993

"Incarnation of a Hiroshima Woman"

TITLE:

The BOOK OF PHI
Volume 5

SUB-TITLE:

PHI CODE 2
(The MULTI-DIMENSIONAL POWERS OF PHI)

(The 2nd of 3 Primal ParaPhysical Phi Code 108 Dials
that Generate the 72 ArcAngelic Names of God)

Author:

Jain 108

Self-Published:

12~12~2012

Made in the USA
Monee, IL
20 February 2021